GIRLS

will be

GW00569183

GRILS

by Bryn Purdy, B.Phil.Ed. (failed)

© 1989

A fictive documentary about a community of
adolescent girls under stress,
written by its Head Care Taker and Assistant Caretaker

———————————

Published by
The Laneill Press, 50 Holbrook Road, Belper, Derbyshire DE5 1PB

Contents

Girls will be Grils 3

Caveat Lector 5

The Conceiving of a Manuscript 7

Man Behind the Camera 10

Moot Points 17

A Case of Buggery in a Girls' School? 23

An Unlikely Applicant 27

The Artful Dodger Lives 28

The Case of the Phantom Scratcher 31

The Case of the Phantom Snatcher 33

An Inspector Calls 37

Nell: *A Correspondance Verité*, including 37
     An Induced Lull: An Inspector Palls 47

Runaways 60

By the Grace of . . . Providence? 62

Guarding a Confidence 64

Protecting One's Image 65

Trouble Up At t'Mill 68

A Moment of Truth 69

To Mansfield 74

The Curious Incident of the Dog in the Night 76

Contradictions 83

Nuit de l'Enfer 87

Christmas Spirit 92

A Policeman's Lot 95

A Paternal Gift 101

God's Excuse: a Theological Colloquy 103

From Mansfield to Bournemouth 106

Messering About 106

Mootivation 107

A Belittling Life 111

An Opportunity for Counselling 117

A Rare Branch of the Martial Arts Leads to an Act of Disarming 118

A Wild-Gril Chase 122

Woman in Camera 125

De Profundis 130

Birth of a Book 133

GIRLS WILL BE GRILS

Several years ago, I heard a radio programme discoursing on The Graffito.

One of the anecdotes became especially meaningful for me. Someone had written starkly on a toilet wall, with comparative verbal restraint, but ill-spelt, and in characters clumsy and ill-formed:

I WANT A GRIL.

Below, a subsequent visitant to this shrine of self-expression had added, in an educated hand, and, one may imagine, with pursed lips:

YOU MEAN A 'GIRL', DON'T YOU?

And, lower still, in a third hand, the letters deliberately distorted and writhing till the legend ended nearer to floor-level:

WHAT ABOUT US GRILS?

It amused me at the time, but, subsequently, I have speculated about the nature of the Gril, about the kind of possibly hermaphrodite creature who would dare enter a male toilet and declare itself so brazenly.

Since those innocent days of the mid-seventies, I have had occasion to meet many a gril in the course of my subsequent professional life as Care Taker in a residential school for girls under stress. She will present herself in the appearance and form of a perfectly normal girl: attractive, friendly, courteous, fond of babies and animals. Under certain circumstances, however, the perfectly normal girl will transmogrify herself into a gril: frenzied, occasionally violent, termagant, shrill and extensively foul-mouthed — a gril.

So if the word 'gril' be found in the subsequent text, it will be understood that it is not a type-setter's error. If we make allowance for the male-child's high spiritedness with the old saw that 'boys will be boys', then may not girls sometimes be grils?

3

A Page Dedicatory

To A.S.Neill (and Lo! Abu ben Neill's name led all the rest), who determined the kind of teacher I became (qv pp. 14-15).

To Greg, who must accept responsibility for my having become a teacher at all (qv p. 14).

To Meg, without whom the daily life of the school over the years would lose its heart, and I have none for the running of it (passim throughout, particularly pp. 125-130).

To Neil, Deputy Head Care Taker and Head Caretaker, who runs affairs during my not infrequent absences of mind from school.

To Colleagues-and-Friends and the Befrienders of Rowen House School, whom it were invidious to identify individually.

To the Disc between my third and fourth vertebrae, without whose sudden and agonising 'slipping' I would not have had the enforced leisure to begin this book (qv p 7).

To Our Girls, who did not allow the stress of circumstance to occlude their zest for life, and without whom there would have been no book to write, I dedicate all the remaining pages in affection and respect.

B. F.

CAVEAT LECTOR

Before you lay down good money for this chunk of print, allow me to advise you as to its matter, and counsel you particularly as to whether the manner of its telling may be to your taste.

Its matter is a series of snap-shots, episodes from the daily life of a community of girl-youths under stress. The episodes were chosen because of their narrative flow and dramatic turns of event, because of the real wit and sometimes unconscious humour of their protagonists. However, incident in itself has not been my aim: it is when event highlights character, or when character defines event, that I have made an exposure, photographically speaking.

Having advised you about the matter, I caution you against the manner of its telling, which may offend the fastidious and deprave the susceptible.

Firstly, while I declare that I have tried to portray our community in its moods of tears, anger and laughter — and, withal to remain cheerful myself — I'm afraid that philosophy was always breaking in. The schoolmaster in me would out. The book as a whole may have no didactic purpose, but the author has his pedagogical concerns, reflections and irritations. I caution you to beware his blandishments to come up and see his professional itchings when he has felt compelled to scratch them in print.

Secondly, I regret that the author has indulged his foible for the borrowed, tinted light of literary allusion, but, for the most part, he has spared you tedious attributions and fussy footnotes. So you must not be surprised to find the occasional, familiar glint of gold melded into the coarser metal of his prose.

Thirdly, a particular caution to the morally and linguistically sensitive. The author is not describing the daily life of a Finishing School for the Daughters of Gentlefolk (although it may have much in common with one, for all I know).

In the pressure-cooker of our society, we get into quite a stew at times over the functions of the human body; anatomical, excretory and reproductive. When, therefore, the safety-valve blows, we must not be surprised, much less shocked, when the stew hits the ceiling — when, if I may sanitize a current Americanism, the stew hits the fan. The form of the explosion of feeling in the disturbed person is in words, obscene words, words which may give offence. The children of our society did not invent the words: they were taught them. Perhaps I owe it to the prospective purchaser of this book to explain the author's attitude to this interesting psychological and linguistic phenomenon.

The traditional educator accepted that children might be obscene as long as they were not heard; the progressive educator of a later generation argued the child's right to be heard to be obscene. I tack a middle course. A quarter of a century ago, I recognised the need for pent children to ventilate and discharge their disturbance in obscenities, to be free to swear. I still do, but over the years my practice has been to encourage the child to free herself of the habit, easefully over the months, not immediately prohibitively. My aim is that the child shall be free also **not** to swear.

It would not be accurate to portray such a community as I describe in the following pages without some of the spices of language, as well as its stodge. **Nell: A Correspondance Verité** may be considered a particularly hot curry in this respect. Apart from that, the most delicate palate need not come to harm if you will not bite upon the occasional chili, but put it to the side of the plate.

The Conceiving of a Manuscript

I am heavy with book. More like twins by the feel of it. Not the trim, square-cut, finished artefact which you are holding in your hands now, but its ill-formed, shapeless manuscript foetus which weighed me down then, 3 years ago as I sat wondering whether to abort or bring to life. Very early on I asked the advice of experts in bookbirth. They scanned the foetus and found that they couldn't foresee a commercially healthy baby at the end of a full-term pregnancy. (It was some years later that I learnt that one of these experts, The Virago Press, had a conscientious obstetric objection to bookbearing by males).

Of course, we all respect the advice of experts in any field, but one does not have to take it. Have I not myself, in the capacity of a guardian of teenage girls, often advised the pregnant young woman to have an abortion or at least to have the child adopted?

It transpires that I can't take the advice I have so convincingly offered others. Now I understand why. So what if a proper gynaecological publishing hospital will not accept the responsibility, then I must employ my own wet-nurse printer. What if it should bring shame on its parent, or, worse for a devout solitary like myself, what if it should bring renown? No matter, it has a right to life; it must make its own way in the world, or be remaindered.

It began several years ago. I admit I encouraged the idea. I cannot deny that I actually flirted with it. I had no experience in these affaires. I had never written a book before, so I had no thought of the heartache and travail it would cause me . . .

But I should have known better, I know. My only excuses are that I had business worries from which I needed distraction, and that the disc between my third and fourth vertebrae had burst or 'slipped', so I was lying painfully and helplessly flat on my back with my knees raised, as my Alexander Practitioner had instructed me. I couldn't go anywhere. I couldn't do anything. I was bored. And then . . . it happened. One minute I was thinking about my business worries . . . and the next . . . the idea for this manuscript was conceived . . .

But the chances of an actual birth seemed unlikely and, in any case, remote, so I fell to pondering my financial difficulties. You see, 1985 had been a bad trading year for us. When our accountant came to see my wife and me in October, I asked him when 'overdraft' became 'debt', and at what point 'debt' should be declared 'bankruptcy'.

Meg and I listened uncomprehendingly as he talked 'collateral', 'assets' and 'market forces'. Our strong point is not finance; our trade is teaching. For 15 years we had ticked over on a State salary, never going into the red, carefully husbanding our resources. Then, six years ago, we had mortgaged an old Edwardian orphanage, unsaleable for normal residential purposes and empty for years, and pursued our educational specialism of care-taking disturbed children.

They had been exciting years, but exhausting to the point where each holiday was not so much recreation as recuperation. So exciting that I used to exhort our pupils to write it all down, so that they could read about themselves in years to come; so exhausting that no conscientious member of staff had the residual energy to do it himself.

Our pupils never did it, and they may have thought, with Stevenson, that books are a mighty bloodless substitute for life — although their actual words on the subject were more likely to be those of Philip Larkin. I had no time or energy for it — until 1985, when a trade recession hit our miniscule corner of the market, and I had time on my hands.

I had told all the staff in March that if things continued the way they were going, we should have to economise. Our main stock-in-trade was human resources, so human resources would have to be the first to go, to enable the school to survive.

But of course, I assured them, it shouldn't come to that. Crisis of one sort or another had become a way of life. We had survived flourished bread-knives, marauding drunken youths, the resignation of core-staff at a fortnight's notice, even a week-end's notice, attempted suicide, multiple absconding, five-figure overdrafts, no cigarettes on a Sunday — we had survived them all. But by July our numbers had dropped to below a third of those which we needed to maintain the viability of the school.

With time on my hands, I had to think about the future. Perhaps I ought to write articles for learned journals, to inform the right people about the service we were offering to children under stress. But learned articles are not my style. I do not read them, and have no taste for writing them. When educational psychologists visiting the school ask me theoretical questions, I respond with an apposite anecdote, usually from the past week, often from the past 24 hours. Let them draw their own inferences.Partly this habit is a personal distaste for acting as my own Public Relations man, as I am aware that the theory may not honestly represent the practice, and partly because of a personal predeliction for the narrative.

Given the present threatened state of the school, and my own under-employed time, may the account of the saga of dramatic and humorous incidents not be grist to the mill of the school's future? And if the protagonists in my story will not put pen to paper, I must do it myself. In the words of a favoured essayist of my teen-years:'Every man his own Boswell'. Would such an account be readable? . . . saleable?

What might the nature of such an account be? Clearly, if it purports to be the truth, it may not be the whole truth, which would be prolix. It must not be nothing-but-the-truth, as its publication might give pain. Why not then write a fictional account, which would protect the identity of the protagonists? Again, it may be a matter of taste, but I cannot read fiction these years, much less write it: and, as the man said when he deplored sex and violence on television, I have too much fiction in my everyday life, as the following pages may indicate. They contain coincidences, turns of event and interventions of God or Providence which few novelists, aiming at verisimilitude, would dare to employ.

If truth were my goal, my end, what shall be my means, the form of the account?

It was a re-reading of **The Best Loved Game** at this time which was the germ for the idea of the form of my projected manuscript. After a richly adventurous life, Geoffrey Moorhouse returned to England yet again in 1977 to realise that a new materialism was bidding to take over the game of cricket, bat, ball and stumps — that Packerism was threatening to destroy the idyll that began in Hambledon.

Moorhouse's book is a lovingly-observed and finely-etched set of verbal prints, portraying all levels of the summer game's days in the sun of 1977.

I perceived melancholy parallels to my own situation. My specialism of care-taking children under stress is to ordinary classroom education what the modern one-day game of cricket is to the traditional three-day County Championship, as played by W. G. Grace, Wilfred Rhodes, Frank Woolley, Percy Fender, Percy Nunn, Fred Trueman, Fred Clarke, R. H. Spooner, H. C. Dent, W. H. Hadow, R. J. O. Meyer, George Gunn, George Sampson — superb stylists, both these Georges — and many another Gentleman and Player.

Why had I not contented myself with the civilised pedestrian pace of the three-day game? Why had I not been satisfied to communicate to young, eager minds the excitement of learning: the meaning of number, the cumulative power of language, an awareness of the sempiternality of the Past-Present-and-Future? Could I not have spent many a happy, liberating hour on field excursions, showing children from some chosen vantage-point the relationship of the Ordnance Survey symbols with the landscape stretched out below us? Back in the classroom, could I not have compared these maps with the wondrous accuracy of their forerunners of 1930, 1910, 1880 and 1848? Could I not have compared them with the beauteous inaccuracies of the maps of 1789, 1648 and 1610?

All these minor but cultivated and edifying pleasures of the classroom I had forgone for the knockabout thrills of the one-day game, for the emotional, sometimes physical, eyeball-to-eyeball confrontation, the disturbing, uncouth sledging from these slips of girls to counterpoint even one's finest strokeplay, for the risky gamble made under pressure of time, which could win or lose the game.

It's much more exciting than what happens in the classroom, of course, but . . . but as the Ordinary School Headmaster might say of our Special School junketings, "C'est magnifique, mais c'est n'est pas l'éducation".

And the very excitement of the game is exhausting over the years, as Ian, David and Graham are finding, as I pen these lines in this bicentennial year of Our Lords, 1987.

For me too what had been a pleasure has become at times only a livelihood, and I had felt as toad-ridden by work as any day-labourer. Necessarily a livelihood, I could, however, look back on glorious moments, momentous days, halcyon weeks.

I could at least make a record, as Moorhouse had done, of however many months were vouchsafed the ebbing life of the school.

So it was that I decided to begin a journal, recording the incidents of each day, week and month of the academic year 1985/6.

I actually put pen to paper in the waiting-room of the casualty ward of the local hospital towards the end of the first week. My delayed start had been due to a rather busy 4 days. When I had chronicled the concerted harassment of one girl by several others; when I had chronicled the outing during which I had to pull the car over on to the grass verge when one girl insulted, then attacked, a second; and I had to hold them ungently apart while claws flailed; when I had chronicled the deliberate smashing of a large window and the rushing to hospital of a lacerated girl; when I had chronicled the riot which led to the calling in of the Police (while I was peacefully writing up my journal in the aforesaid casualty ward); when I had chronicled being told about the suicide of a dear friend and former colleague . . . When I had chronicled all these events encompassed within four days, I realised that the augurs for the journal-form were not propitious. It might be the kind of life I was leading during those few days, but it was not the kind of book which it would give me any pleasure to write.

No, I had neither the time, the stamina, nor the temperament to write a laboriously detailed account of the passing hours, weeks and months of a single year: I would instead pond-dip my memory for events and aspects of character which seemed significant to me. Significant to me, for my account does not purport to be the Whole Truth; only the *cinema verité* of the man behind the camera.

Man Behind the Camera
Academic Credentials

I have attained my ideal. I am become the Head Care Taker in a school for Children under Stress. Some say Headmaster. Both titles are correct, but the one is more pregnant than the other.

I suppose that it is not inappropriate that the Head Care Taker in a school for children who have failed in the Educational System (or whom the Educational System has failed) should himself be an academic failer. I write 'failer' because although I have an almost unblemished record of failing in scholastic exams, I have never *felt* a 'failure' in the wider sense. If I think about this, it may be because I am almost impervious to what I am told is a basic human instinct, that of competitiveness.

The last time that I can remember caring whether I succeeded or failed, won or lost, was in the school sports of 1944. The Primary Heats had been run off and four times another boy called Swan and I had come first and second. I remember Swan as a swarthy, muscled young man of eight. (The reader need not fear a too subtly proustian evocation of childhood here. The boy's name **was** Swan, with one 'n', and the only boy I can remember from that Class of '44. It has stayed in my mind over the years: I record it). Since I had come First and Swan Second in each Heat, if only by a whisker, it was presumed that I would win the Final. I can still hear Swan's striving breaths just behind me on each occasion. I was confident of victory. Sports Day dawned. Swan won the Final. It may have been because he was a better runner; it may have been because, sharing the loneliness of a long distance runner of a later generation, I simply truanted from the arena and went exploring the woods and hills behind my County Down home.

My career was greatly promoted by another quality without which the true aspirant in the great School of Failing cannot succeed: I was impervious to being taught.

(Perhaps even at this early age I had preceived the truth of Rimbaud's dictum that "All that we are taught is false". This may seem nihilistic, but is the corollary of that very positive truth for which I will hold no one, not even Rimbaud, responsible: All that we learn is true. I forbear to pursue the quarry of an idea into the thicket of paradox: All that we learn, even when it is 'false', is true).

My mother found me so difficult to teach to read at the age of nine that I was sent to a Preparatory boarding school, where I failed Common Entrance to Public School. I was whisked away from my expensive private education, and sat the 11 + exam. Failed again. My mother who was a very persuasive woman, interceded with the Authorities: they told her I had failed the exam and that was an end on't. My mother, who was a very persistent woman, made an appointment to see the Chief Officer of Education, and I became the only child in Derbyshire who, having failed the 11 +, went on to attend Grammar School.

Alas, Mr. Jack Longland's faith in me was not justified, in performance at least, and I failed all my 'O' levels except that in my mother tongue.

It was some relief to realise that my schooling, my being taught, was over. Everybody was very brave about it, especially me. And then a great and beneficial miracle befell me, not for the last time in my life in the guise of a great misfortune. Not that I ever saw it for anything other than the greatest of good fortune, even when the specialist came to pronounce his expert diagnosis beside my hospital bed, even after my weeping relatives had been shown out of the ward and I had been placed behind screens in the corner, with cutlery and crockery marked freshly with my name. What to others might have seemed, and in many cases was, a death sentence, was to me a reprieve from an uncongenial office job. What had the man said? At least 3 months' Bed Rest? Probably six. I must prepare my mind to spend "at least 12 months in a sanatorium . . ." What bliss of freedom . . . "probably 2 years". My cup runneth over . . .

11

I did not know then about spes phthisica, the last stage in the career of the disease tuberculosis, when the patient experiences a sudden short-lived burst of hope, the last sparkle before life gutters out.

Within a few days, or it may have been hours, I was rushed to a sanatorium where I was the only patient too ill to watch the Coronation on T.V. a day or two later. I didn't mind. I was already deep into **Lost Horizon,** and knew I had found my Shangri La. My twice-daily dose of streptomycin saved my life while I read about how drugs had ruined the Opium-Eater's. While this powerful new drug was saving my body, another, even more heady, was at work upon my mind. A school-friend had slipped me a couple of phials on a visit to the hospital, and, after a first bitter-sweet tasting which was by no means agreeable, I found myself 'hooked', to use the idiom of a future decade. Its immediate effect was the hallucination of being transported across a warp of time — into Georgian London, to be precise. Following the markings originally made by Bozzie's asiduous quill, I spent long evenings at the Mitre Tavern and, in my mind, companioned the Grand Cham through dark streets, lit only irregularly by sputtering rush-and-tar lamps, to tread the adze-hewn floor-boards of his house in Gough Square — a visit I was to make, many years later, wandering, a fleshly revenant, through the hallowed rooms.

While my body in the sanatorium suffered the tablets and injections of a welcome fate, my 17-year-old imagination had its first vivid experience of time-travel. Since I opened the first volume on visiting day, which was Sunday, I had lived through sixty-five years, from 1709 to 1774. Then, one morning in the middle of next week, to my great dismay, I realised that I had finished the first volume, and that there were only 618 grains left in the second phial. I would have to ration my use of the drug — not that I feared the addiction, which did in fact become life-long, but that the magic wouldn't last and I would have to return to live within my body. But I resolved to cut it down to 30 grains per day, and prolonged the enchantment, albeit in a weakened strain, for a further three weeks.

In the meantime, I had come across another hallucinogen, which induced a quite other illusion: having experienced time-travel with James Boswell, I began world-travel with George Borrow. And it was Lavengro himself who prompted a curiosity about languages, which, as shall be seen, had a crucial effect on my young manhood.

For the present, I sent away for **Le Compte de Monte Cristo** in the original, and plunged into it without knowing how to swim, with only a pocket dictionary as my compass, and found myself a joyous prisoner on my own Chateau d'If. But it was a cell with three sides, the fourth open to the elements. No Abbé Faria, it is true, but who needs a teacher when one has books? I read **Jude the Obscure** and knew him for a fellow-autodidact.

So began my studentship in this University of the Open Air, some years before something similar was ideated by Harold Wilson.

And then things began to go wrong. True, I was permitted to remain in bed for 12 glorious weeks, as the specialist had promised me. But to talk about having to be rusticated from my alma mater after only 9 months was against the terms of contract of my admission. The man had said I could stay for at **least** one year, probably two. My room-mate, Denis, had been here two already and there was no talk about **his** being turfed out. And that chap down the corridor who had been here four years, and my friend Ronnie for six. Six when I arrived, so it must be nearer seven now. I was half way through Borrow's **Bible in Spain**, and had only just begun **Las Confesiones de un Pequeño Filósofo**. Did I *have* to go?

The doctor was very kind to me and explained that I had adapted myself so well to sanatorium life that my case was the most remarkable cure, from a standing — or rather a supine — start, that he had encountered in his professional career. It was then that I ceased to expect fairness from Life. A lot of other chaps spent their time complaining about life in a sanatorium, and they had to stay. I was learning to enjoy it thoroughly, and I was having to leave.

It was decided that I could have a further extension of sentence for good conduct, and I was discharged 12 months to the day after my admission.

It might be supposed that I had become a little rusty in the art of academic failing, but I became a sanatorium nurse as part of my convalescence. I kept my hand in by failing a few more exams by the way, and a mutual decision with the authorities was made to leave the profession.

I skate over the next period in my life. I ran no risk of passing exams, because for six years I did not take any. I became a *plongeur* in the sculleries of French hotels, a Youth Hostel Warden in Geneva, a fairground worker and farm labourer in France and Germany. The while I had been earning the odd Franc or Mark in teaching English to foreigners, and I began to think that there might be a livelihood in the trade. Having experienced some difficulty in one European capital, I was advised that finding a job as a teacher might be easier if I dressed . . . differently, and, more importantly, if I were qualified. To be qualified I would need a certain number of 'O' levels to enter college. To show that my mind had risen above any vulgar prejudice against academic success, I popped back to England, passed a few exams, mostly in languages I had taught myself, and, still to keep my hand in, failed Eng. Lit. I found myself still wanting one 'O' level to enter college, so I wintered in Spain, teaching English and learning Spanish, and returned to complete the minimal qualifications for entering College of Education. I would qualify myself, and then resume my vagabondage, taking my chance of livelihood where it might lie, with the trade of teaching my own language throughout the whole world to fall back on, to native-speakers or foreigners.

The youth who had left the sanatorium was very different from the young man who entered College of Education. My life may have lain fallow of any vocational purpose for five years, but my mind had been harrowed and cross-harrowed by the different ideas and cultures, the joys and sorrows, to which it had become exposed. Early in my student life it became apparent that nothing could be planted in it. I could **learn** perhaps, but I could not be **taught.** Perhaps the tilth was too fine; perhaps the soil adverse. Then scruples began to assail me. I was conscious of accepting public money for my training for a profession which I realised that I had a diminishing intention of practising.

I'd better get out, I supposed, despite the seductive, hand-warm comfort of three meals a day, a roof over my head at night, a library within walking distance, all found, and a student grant, which, in those palmy days of the early sixties, was adequate to my spartan needs. All too comfortable perhaps, too tepid. I had become accustomed to the stimulus of the unexpected, even of the adverse. No, I can't stand another two and a half years. How to effect my withdrawal? I'll go and see Mr. Gregory. He is for me the most approachable of my tutors. He'll tell me how to get unfrocked, or ungowned, without dishonour to either side and at the least inconvenience. So, having rehearsed a series of impregnable arguments why I should leave College as soon as possible, I presented myself at his study door by appointment.

Greg listened to my reasoning attentively, with eyes fixed on the worn carpet between us. When I finished, there was a short silence, then he lifted his head and looked at me smilingly in the eyes:

"Why don't you just accept free bed and board for the next couple of years, irrespective of how you spend your time, pick up a ticket at the end of the 3 years, and then you can decide what you do with the rest of your life?"

I had anticipated a range of logical arguments, based on wordly wisdom which might have been presented to me, to each of which I had a steel-reinforced answer. But the preposterous amorality of Greg's proposal left me speechless. Taking my speechlessness for the silence which assents, Greg warmed to his thesis.

"You do enjoy study, don't you, as long as it's on your own terms. I'm your main subject tutor. That subject embraces such a wide area that even mavericks like yourself can surely find a piece of prairie to graze on.

"Your ambition may not lie in teaching, but the qualification will be useful to you in some related field. I think you have something to offer, and I'd like to help you fulfil yourself while you're in this College . . ."

It seemed that, without having returned a word to this downy old bird, I had committed myself to a self-designed programme of study under his benign academic aegis.

Even the self-designed programme presented itself shortly afterwards, even though it had nothing to do with teaching. There was this dotty old Scotsman who ran an unschool in rural Suffolk. We all knew about him, didn't we? I myself had written him off as a potentially dangerous eccentric when I read an article about him in the popular press in my early teens. He ran the do-as-you-like-school, where there are no classes, no religious observance, where the children can smoke, where they can first-name the teachers. The man sounded cracked to me. But is he? His books

14

themselves have a curiously plausible ring to them, if one suspends from one's mind conventional good sense. He implements a practice of Freedom for children which Shelley only dared to postulate for adults, and John Stuart Mill, high-priest of Libertarianism, positively discommended for children.

The canon of his ideas, by turns penetratingly shrewd and ingenuously tendentious, gnawed at my mind. I'll have to go down to the school, meet this Wild Old Man of the Educational Woods, and work him and his crazy ideas out of my system.

So I did visit Summerhill, and, as a potentially dangerous visitor, was permitted to install my sleeping-bag and rucksack in the farthest outbuilding in the school grounds. By mid-week I was invited into the more comfortable Theatre to sleep, and by the end of the fortnight was ensconced not only in an empty dormitory in the main school building at night, but was teaching in the Old Man's classroom itself during the school day, to give him a welcome break from the G.C.E. syllabus.

You may wonder what conclusions this resident of three weeks and visitor during three years arrived at over A. S. Neill. My teenage opinion was confirmed. As someone said about a much greater visionary of the human condition, "The man **was** cracked, of course — that is where the Light came in".

The light of the Summerhill Idea had a crucial effect on my own career. It became the subject of my total study for the remainder of my 3 years at College and totally unfitted me to work in ordinary sensible schools for the rest of my professional life. My study of Summerhill not only blighted my career but is the one major tarnish on my record of Failing which it is the object of this essay to establish. The supervising University awarded me an academic Distinction for my 3-year absorbtion in Summerhillism, which must have been a bit embarassing for the College authorities, because I was still running true to form in other subjects. True I had at last passed Eng. Lit., but I had failed the least specifically academic subject of all — Physical Education, not once, but twice, and my friends lamented that my whole college career was to be voided for the want of this component piece of paper.

I remember the sequence well. The first time I sat in the large Assembly Room with several hundred other aspirants to P.E. expertise I was the only failer in the college — in any subject.

On the second occasion I went to a small room in Manchester with a dozen or so other shuffling, nerve-wracked failers of **all** subjects from the whole of the North-West of England — and failed again.

This experience did, however, vouchsafe me an interesting insight into the whole examinational rationale. One of the other candidates showed me his paper in French. I scanned it, and decided that I stood more chance of passing this subject, which I hadn't seriously studied for 4 years, than the one which I had studied in my desultory, lacklustre way for the last two.

The Vice Principal welcomed my proposal as at last evidence of some ambition.

"But I'm afraid **not.** You see, this College doesn't offer French".

"Yes, I know, but the supervising University must do".

"Yes, I believe it does, but we don't in**vig**ilate it".

"Yes, but you — I mean this college — didn't invigilate me the second time when I went to Manchester".

"Yes, but we prepared you for that exam. We haven't pre**par**ed you for French, You haven't attended a **course** in the subject".

"No, but I didn't attend a **course** on the 'O' level subjects I passed to enter College in the first place. But I **knew** enough to pass. Surely it is my **knowledge** of French which is at issue, not how I **acquired** it".

"Yes, but . . ."

I had been engaged in sufficient "yes-but-no" conversations during the past few years not to know when I was beaten.

So I went to sit the exam a **third** time. I will not claim to be the only failer in the North West — perhaps my sequestration was felt necessary to prevent contagion — but I sat scribbling away in a little room with a bored invigilator my only company.

From my subsequent interview with my tutor I gathered that I had not so much passed as . . . well . . . not failed. Perhaps, he suggested, it would be as well not to take up P.E. as my specialism. Anyway, I was a qualified teacher.

Fourteen years passed, of which I had spent ten as a Head Care Taker of State schools for children under stress, before my next essay into academic failing, when I joined a year's University Course.

Surely at last I had matured sufficiently not to fail again. If I had intended to fail, the augurs were bad. My tutor warned me at interview that I was one of the best-read candidates to the specialism that it had been his pleasure to welcome on to his course. During an early lecture, another told our group that no one had ever failed it since its inclusion on the syllabus of the University. We were all experienced teachers, carefully culled from the ranks of the aspiring, expected to fill high executive posts. We were all chosen so carefully as to exclude the possibility of failure. The University was unlikely to admit that it had been wrong in its original selection.

At the end of the year, however, the University published its lists and established its integrity and, no doubt, discernment by naming two failers. An African gentleman, with no very sure grasp of the idiom of our richly contradictory tongue, sought me out for consolation. I reassured him that we would do better when we re-sat the exam in a month's time. He parted from me smilingly with evidently greater confidence, and when we three, including the invigilator, met in a small room the following month, he seemed cheerful. I sincerely hope that my little pep-talk did him some good, as it would be some consolation to me in this latest episode of my failing. I do not want it to be thought that I **disdained** to pass: disdaining is for more generous and otherworldly natures than mine had become in my early forties with a wife and two children to support. No, I really wanted to pass, **expect**ed to pass; was prepared to sit the exam again in order to do so. The University, however, had made no allowance for such hebetude as mine, and that was the end of my formal education. I had to accept that some men are born to Failing, some achieve It, and some have It thrust upon them.

But to the future! Having now failed at the highest level, demonstrating that academic failing was no mere youthful quirk, was I not qualified — nay, uniquely qualified — to superintend a community for the unschoolable? Let's to it, as Ibsen's Dr. Stockman declared to his sons, in even more ignominious circumstances:

> ". . . I'll try to make free, noble-minded men of you. And we'll have a school. I must have at least 12 to begin with . . .
>
> "Don't you know any street-urchins — any regular ragamuffins? . . .
>
> ". . . Bring me a few of them. I want to experiment with the street-curs for once; there are sometimes excellent heads among them . . ."

Moot Points

It was one clear September morning in 1979, Year of the Child. The new school, named after a nineteenth century educational innovator and utopian, had been open less than 24 hours. The four girls were of different ages, from 12 to 15, of different skin pigmentation, from different parts of England, and their forms of speech were nearly incomprehensible to each other. They manoeuvred around each other, and away from the adults, as if each were a magnet with two unlike poles.

At breakfast-time on our first full day, we mentioned that we all, staff and children, would meet together in the sitting/dining/classroom which was the only one so far furnished, albeit secondhand. The adults sat chatting for nearly half-an-hour till the last of the girls presented herself, and stood with her back to the open door. No, she wouldn't sit down, thank you very much. She was busy, and had just called to see what was going on.

"Oh, I see, Dierdre. Well, don't feel obliged to stay if you've something better to do. I just thought that we might all have a chat together. Ray, Fran, Meg and I have had time to get to know each other over the past fortnight while we've been scrubbing floors, moving furniture, making beds — literally making beds, I mean, with nuts and bolts, using spanners. So we have got to know, respect, and like each other, and I want us all to feel the same now that we are going to live together.

"The first thing you will have realised is that the staff address each other

17

by our first names and we'd like to invite you to do the same. We want to be as close to you as are good friends, as affectionate with you as are good parents, and for you to be as fond of each other as good sisters".

At this point the fire-door swung to loudly and we all turned to find Dierdre regarding me with a look which clearly said: This man is the ultimate Bore, but I will stay so that it does not divest me of my inalienable rights. No, she wouldn't sit down, and neither did she thank me this time. She takes up a position, standing against a cupboard with an expression of studied nonchalance on her face.

"Well, I'll carry on to tell you one or two things about this school to avoid later misunderstanding. It is a Special School for Children Under Stress, or rather", as I felt Diedre's eyes boring into my neck, "for Young **Women** under Stress, for none of you is a child any more".

So I began my preamble, choosing the appropriate technical word, as one professional would when talking to his fellows, as my custom has been throughout my career, explaining it where necessary, to mint a currency of communication between us.

"Now, most types of Special School are for irremediable disabilities, like slow learners, the deaf, and the blind, who are·helped to come to terms with their disability without much hope that it shall ever be cured. But children who come to **this** type of Special School are essentially normal, mentally and physically — but they have been subjected to such a degree of stress to their emotions that they are incapable of conducting their life effectively. Their feelings have been so wounded that they have got to go to a kind of educational . . . First Aid Post for treatment. The bad thing about Stress is that invariably, without any exception, it causes the deep pain of personal unhappiness, which is something which blindness, deafness or slow learning may not do: the good thing is that the Child Under Stress is **wounded** not **maimed.** Stress is remediable. It can be treated, and you can recover totally from its ill-effects. As totally, that is to say, as any human being may do, because we are all of us subject to stress or unhappiness to a greater or lesser degree throughout our lives".

There is a tension in the air that warns me that I may not pursue this theme any deeper, although only boredom can be seen on the faces visible to me. Behind me the scrape of a chair suggests that Diedre has sat down.

"So, what are the ways in which we aim to help relieve Stress?"

"One key-word to the solution of this problem is, in my opinion, Confidence, or Self-Confidence: Confidence in your Self. I want you to have confidence to lead your own life, to make decisions about your future, to become the kind of person you want to become, to fulfil yourself.

"A second key-word is Trust, which is only another way of saying 'confidence in other people'. I want us to become acquainted with each other, learn to like each other, become sensitive to the uniqueness that is in each of us, be able to respond to each other. Able to respond: responsible. I want each of us to be responsible, individually and communally. At present, you probably don't know me well enough to trust me. You wouldn't allow me to be on your side. You wouldn't want to be on mine. So let's have a side in common. May I invite you to use my room to get to know me and to get to know each other? There is no Headmaster's Study, only a Common Room.

"That leads me to a third key-idea: Sharing Responsibility. I invite each of you to share in the responsibility of running this school. It's your school. It is here for **your** benefit and happiness. We don't pretend to have all the answers: we need your advice.

"That doesn't mean that we the adults will abdicate our responsibility towards you. The more adult you are, the more share of responsibility for running your own lives you will be accorded. It would be dishonest and unrealistic not to declare that I reserve the right to **restrain** you **from** anti-social behaviour, but I do not foresee situations where I shall need to **coerce** you **to** do something to which you have a conscientious objection".

I paused to allow for response, and surveyed our new pupils. They severally sat or slumped in attitudes which bespoke their complete alienation from what I was saying. There was no response, so I continued.

"My silence just now was meant to indicate my readiness to listen to what you have to say".

The girls looked at each other momentarily, as if expecting a lead from one of them, but resumed their attitudes without speaking, lacklustre.

"The way in which I propose to build up confidence and trust, and to learn how to share responsibility is to meet together each day to talk with each other. A kind of school assembly, a forum where we can all have the freedom to talk and exchange ideas. Each morning you may choose to come to this room at about 9.30 to attend the Moot. 'Moot' only means 'Meeting'. It's an Anglo-Saxon word, which means 'a collection of Freemen'. I like it because it survives in English today mainly in the phrase 'a moot-point', which means that an issue is debatable; there can be more than one way of looking at it. When friends disagree, they can simply stop arguing and continue their friendship by declaring, that's a moot point".

Angela stares at me hard, as if my whole discourse might have been couched in Anglo-Saxon, for all the import it held for her.

"Each morning any of us is free to raise his or her own 'moot-point' to discuss in the Moot. In my experience of Moots, which I have been attending for as long as any of you has been alive, they will last for about an hour each day. In my early days we used to have a lot of voting to resolve majority decisions, but more recently I have found people more ready to arrive at decisions by consensus when everyone ends basically in agreement. In my early days the Moot was more like a Court whose purpose was to mete out Punishments, or, as I prefer to call them, 'Consequences' for wrong-doing. As I've grown older and either wiser or softer-in-the-head, I have witnessed the Moot changing its character. Of recent years it has talked more and judged less. If a child feels that he or she will not be 'punished' for a misdemeanour, she is much more ready to acknowledge it.

"You may well ask what we shall be conversing about for an hour each morning. And I can assure you it won't be me rabbiting on like I am today. No, within a week or two we all shall be exchanging ideas and expressing our feelings. When I wrote to each of you during the Summer Holidays before we had met, I asked you what you liked doing and what would be your ideal school, that is, how you would like a school to be run if *you* had *your* way. Each of you was able to tell me the things you liked doing, but none of you answered the second question.

"Well, that's what our Moots are going to be about. The school that *you'd* like. In fact, here's a book to give you a few ideas. It's written by children and young men and women, and it's called just that: **The School that I'd Like.** I'll leave it around.

"Now let me explain what the Moot is *not.* It is not Telling Tales. From early childhood you've been told not to 'tell tales' by adults who have not had time to deal with the very real unhappinesses caused by bullying and by other kids who knew they would be punished if their wrong-doing were revealed. No, tale-telling implies going behind another person's back to someone in 'authority', which results in punishment. So, if we all share Authority, as I have explained already, and if we disavow Punishment, then there can be no Tale-Telling, no 'grassing'. I am hoping that we may achieve an atmosphere in which we do not even talk about each other behind our backs, in which we do not gossip about each other.

"So what are we left with? We are left with The Moot, where each of us shares the responsibility for running the school, where each of us may speak openly about our personal happiness, where each of us is free to challenge the behaviour of another member of the community where it affects us individually or communally. We may feel secure in engaging the authority of the Moot to protect our personal rights".

My eyes had been fixed on the rolling hills outside the window while uttering the foregoing, and I arrested myself long enough to wonder whether my discourse, as well as my gaze, had been above their heads. But I was reassured to find four pairs of eyes fixed on me — including Dierdre's, who had moved from behind me to the arm of the sofa from where she could observe at least my half-face.

"I'm sorry if I am sounding like a party political broadcast on the telly, and if the words I am using are . . . high-falutin', but my concern is your personal happiness, each of you, all of us.

"Your personal happiness, particularly regarding Bullying. That goes for me too, of course. I do not wish to run your lives, to coerce you to do things you don't want to do. And that's where the Moot comes in. If you feel I am being bossy or have not kept a promise I have made you, then you must discharge your sense of grievance . . . that is, your feeling of unfairness . . . by raising my actions in the Moot, where I may present my side, and we all may offer our opinions.

20

"By the same token, if any girl is bullied by another, she will raise the matter in the Moot".

My looking around at this point at all the girls happens to catch an exchanged glance between Evelyn and Dierdre, and is my first intimation of the tyrannous hold which one of the girls already has over the other three.

"And when the girl raises the issue of bullying in the Moot, she may expect restitution . . . that means that her grievance shall be put right. Either by a simple apology, the return of the property, or however the Moot may decide".

I paused again, invited comment, but, encouraged by the listening silence, took up my stride once more.

"I don't want you to go away with the impression that the Moot consists of my talking all the time. I hope you will understand that I am taking up a lot of the time today, seeking to explain the kind of school we are aiming at. In fact, I don't even want to be in charge of our Moot. Every Meeting has its Chairman, so our Moot will have its . . . Chair-girl, who will be responsible for maintaining order and keeping things ticking over. I am quite happy now for one of you to take over the Chairgirlship of this Moot and lead the discussion about what each of you wants and expects out of your new school".

The three girls in front of me looked at each other covertly, then at me and then away, as if I were some tasteless Music Hall comedian who had invited them on stage.

I turned my head. "What about you, Dierdre?"

Twelve year old Dierdre stared back at me and made me feel like a Nazi Recruiting Officer at a meeting of the Maquis (although we would have both been surprised if we had had the foreknowledge that within 10 days she would be our first Chair-girl, early faltering, later assured and decisive).

I stared long and hard at a patch of linoleum beyond my feet until I became aware of a restive shifting of limbs. I collected myself and looked into each pair of eyes in turn.

"I have to warn you that there is one thing you may find very disagreeable about your new school". I registered the expressions in the faces ranged before me, and the deeper furrowing of the brows and the more pronounced puckering of the lips did not encourage me to turn and risk the daggers of Dierdre's eyes.

I shook my head sadly. "Yes, the one great disadvantage of this school for some of you at least will be . . . Boredom. And that will arise from what you may be disposed to regard as one of its better aspects: that is, that we shall not coerce you to do anything. You may come to class if you wish, and you'll find that Meg is a very interesting and caring teacher — but we shall not **coerce** you to attend.

"I know that initially this will be very agreeable, that you will feel free to do what you want, and this will immediately remove a bone of contention between you and your teachers, because hitherto a major cause of your dissidence has been teachers' making you behave in class.

"In your new school you will be free not to attend class. You will have the freedom of choice to work or not to work. Now Freedom is a fine word, for which I have a great affection, but as the years have passed I realise that one has to be highly developed mentally and emotionally to fully appreciate and enjoy it. Now I settle for one word to describe Freedom of Choice: Optionality. You will have the option to go to class or go to your bedroom: the more mature person may propose other ways to spend her time which I shall be happy to consider.

"But when you come to take the optionality of class attendance for granted, at least some of you will feel bored. Hitherto, much of your 'interest' in school has been outwitting your teachers over actually attending class or, if you *have* attended, in provoking and defying them, and causing as much disruption as you can. Here I'm afraid we are going to be spoilsports. We are not going to engage ourselves in those kinds of side-games at all. This will cause a vacuum in your interest in life, and this vacuum will lead to Boredom.

"I hope all this talk of 'optionality' and 'not coercing' does not strike you as too negative: in my mind they may be distinctly positive ideas, to the degree that we find ourselves able to respond to them. I hope that you will use the 'free' time you make yourself to opt for responsible goals, to develop your own interests positively, to fulfil yourself.

"If we as staff are happy to 'share our authority' with you so that you are 'free' to do what you wish, we recognise that it is a particular area of our responsibility to Restrain; that is to say, to stop someone who is actually interfering with another person's freedom. This Restraint could take several stages: first, we might suggest that the issue be raised in the Moot the next day; secondly, if this fails, we might ask the person whom *we* consider to be in the wrong to withdraw herself from the situation; thirdly, if that fails, we would *tell* the person to go to her room; and, fourthly, and reluctantly, we are prepared to remove the girl by . . . the laying on of hands".

There was a sharp intake of breath from the direction of Jean, and a hissing "You lay a fuckin' finger on me, mate, an' . . ."

I looked at Jean long and evenly and sought to keep the tenor of my voice easy and friendly.

"I am glad to learn that your repugnance for the laying on of hands is as great as my own, Jean, and", extending my open palms "I sincerely hope that I shall never have to . . . child-handle any of you.

"Let me go on to explain what I mean by 'child-handling', and how it differs from 'man-handling'. On the one hand, 'man-handling' aims to knock the spirit out of someone in order to dominate him. Contrarily, our aim in child-handling is to contain the person who is out of control in as gentle and as pacific a way as she will allow us, and continue to respect her . . . spirit".

My eyes rest on each girl now in turn, and only Jean's are not fixed on

22

mine, as she realises that I will not engage in a staring-match with her.

"Thank you all for listening to me so patiently. But this last point is most important to discuss with you now, since it might arise this week, today, or within the next hour . . . If we do need to restrain a girl, I want you to understand our thinking behind it and our strategy during the period of restraint, however long that may last. The most important thing to bear in mind is that it is not a fight — not a contest; there will be no losers, and only the girl can be a winner when her mind resumes control over her body, and that shall be the sole aim of the restrainers.

"If I have brought this point to your minds so early in our aquaintance, it is because I understand that some of you, perhaps most of you, have had a considerable amount of physical force, including beating, inflicted on you. I declare myself against such treatment, against hitting, against corporal punishment of any kind: I declare myself for responsible behaviour, however, and recognise that a firm strategy of containment may be necessary to effect the happiness of the individual and of the community".

I felt that an albeit brief canter round the triune principles of the French Revolution (or at least the kindred ones of Optionality, Shared Responsibility, and Sorority) was enough for one morning, and I called a break for coffee.

A Case of Buggery in a Girls' School?

The school had been open barely a fortnight. Evelyn was our first-arrived pupil. She was a younger member of a large family whose children had, one after the other, gained a reputation for dissidence in school, and whose adult passages-of-arms with Society were often recorded in the local, and occassionally national, Press.

Even at Infant School Evelyn herself had been made first embarrassingly, then painfully, aware of the mixture of suspicion and antagonism with which she was held by some of her teachers, and, in her hand-down clothes, was early victim of the taunts of her school-fellows.

She responded according to the manner of her tribe by absenting herself from the arena of her suffering. The local Education Welfare Officers compounded her torments over the years in their well-intentioned and good-hearted way. During her early childhood she allowed herself to be led into the pattern of school-going. Subsequently, however, after so many days' absence, the E.W.O. would visit the home and, with that admonitory bonhomie which is part of the personal stock-in-trade of the profession, persuade Evelyn and her mother that "it was for her own good", with a clear intimation that it would **not** be for her own good if she didn't go. Such friendly persuasion had succeeded in so many cases, but when it failed eventually in Evelyn's, the strategy was diversified — and intensified. Regimental morning calls replaced the counselling visits, and Evelyn was led to school each morning to the heavenward glances of her teachers and the titters of her schoolfellows. The front-door rat-tat prompted the stimulus-response of Evelyn's backdoor evasion. An athletic young E.W.O. might be expected to cover both exits, with a rat-tat here and a dash round there, but as Evelyn's determination, truculence and lissomness increased, so was the E.W.O. force doubled. Time and time again was she led into the Arena. With an application of lateral thinking which might have gratified the author of the concept, Evelyn saw the window not only as a means of ventilation or day-time illumination, but of egress, and for a few days had the laugh on her tormentors as she was permitted to rest in peace, protected by a doctor's note testifying to her sprained ankle. But eventually school-going was secured. School-going, but not total attendance, for Evelyn had discovered that, in the Secondary School, she might spend most of her time out of school as long as she obtained her 'mark' at the beginning of each half-day session. It wasn't long before the teachers discovered and commented upon the practice. "What do you expect?" "True to type." "She's going to the bad". Evelyn fulfilled their prophesies and the researchers' predictions that persistent truancy leads to crime.

I was sitting in the administrator's room, our life-earnings for the next 20 years mortgaged in a cold, dank empty building which we hoped to turn into a place of Unlearning & Re-learning, not to mention a viable financial business.

"She's a hard case, Mr Purdy". The Administrator shook his head. "I'll not deny it. Normally we'd have allowed the Law to take its course, but her social worker says he sees something good in her. Quite frankly, what we're trying to do is to place her in some residential establishment where she may be deemed 'maladjusted' before she comes up in Court in a month's time, when assuredly she will be put into detentive care. We've done our best, but none of our usual special schools will touch her. She didn't say a word to one head-master who interviewed her. So, do you think you can handle her?"

Inwardly I sank, but was outwardly buoyant. I sat erect, fingered the unfamiliar tie round my neck, and heard myself joyfully anticipating The Challenge — (after all, we needed the fees!).

For a start, she was not so **large** as my fearfulness had envisioned her. Even as she crouched back into the cushions of our one sofa which we had positioned for visitors, clutching her ill-fitting clothes, knuckles showing white, her figure was obviously slight and her tucked-up stocking-less legs positively skinny. Her face was pinched, pale, and her hair-style, colour, and texture that of the marmalade-jar golliwog.

Her mother sat forward, anxious, friendly. We all sat in the single downstairs furnished room which was to serve as Reception, lounge, dining-and-class-room for our new school, situated in premises built as an orphanage. Clearly it was not tradition which had drawn this parent to the precincts of our private school. Evelyn was, as I have said, our first pupil. No, it was more a fear of her being 'sent away' to one of those Approved School places, her mother explained. It appeared that while Her Majesty may have approved them, Evelyn's mother didn't. Her Reg had returned from one more wild than when he had gone in . . . And, she explained, her husband had not accompanied them to Evelyn's new school because . . . well, they didn't get on together. Mind you, they had been better recently, it appeared, because Evelyn had taken to going out all day to avoid him, and coming home only in the evenings when her father was out.

We tried to bowl some questions to Evelyn herself, but they were all very adroitly fielded and returned by her mother.

I had one disquieting insight into her inner mental state and attitudes while Meg was conversing with her mother. I was looking hard at Evelyn, trying to 'read' her, while her eyes explored the walls and fittings of her new home. At the sound of the word 'father', the perimeter-searchlight of her eyes suddenly focused on me . . . and I realised that I was in the process of fostering a 'daughter' who hated me.

When the interview was drawing to a close, I realised that we hadn't heard Evelyn speak, didn't know the sound of her voice. Not so much a voice as a grunt, we realised as the days elapsed.

"Can I show you to your room, Evelyn?"

"Uh" (which may have meant 'You lead, I follow.')

"Would you like some cauliflower?"

"Uh" ('No, I only like chips')

"Would you like some more sausage?"

"Uh" ('Yes')

"And some more chips?"

"Uh", with some emphasis ('Yes, can't you **see** I'm starving')

"Ten o'clock. Lights out"

"Uh-uh" ('What sort of a doss-'ole is this?')

Really she became quite articulate on the Jew's Harp of her grunt. While she totally ignored her new 'father-figure', she quickly responded to Meg's concern and active care for her physical welfare.

Firstly her aureolate busby was trimmed to fluffy and curly prettiness. Then her whole ward-robe was discarded in favour of new clothes for which we had a maximal grant from her understanding Local Authority. On their return from the shops Meg remarked on the sureness of her sartorial taste. It was probably the first time she had tried on virgin garments. She selected and rejected by a series of aye-grunts and nay-grunts a whole new wardrobe, elegant in each item and congruent as a whole. Had Evelyn the instincts of a lady? She certainly came back from town looking like one. Apart from her composure, that is. For she was wholly dismayed by the initial unrecognition and subsequent joyous expression of admiration by the others. She looked to Meg appealingly, then fled.

As the days elapsed, she continued to relate with the rest of the community through Meg. Another girl who had established herself during the first week as Cock of the School (if girls' schools **have** Cocks, that is: certainly she did the most crowing) had pronounced Evelyn a 'creep', and she was ostracised by the others.

Evelyn did not so much disdain as ignore her new father-figure. But, to employ a deliberate Irishism, I noticed that she allowed her eyes to dwell on me when I was not looking. My subliminal 'reading' of her character led me to an increased liking for her. She was straight. She had integrity. She was mistress of herself, with potential. As yet, she lived in the cellar of the mansion of self that would one day be hers.

I sought my first conversation with her. The day of her court appearance impended and I must communicate the travel arrangements to her. We eyed each other uneasily for different reasons. I wished to express my concern at the outcome of tomorrow's appearance before the Juvenile Magistrates, yet feared to intrude on her privacy.

I explained very slowly and carefully, to allow her to accustom herself to my voice, the times she would be collected and was due in Court. I was pleased to notice that her eyes rested on mine, despite her bowed head and half-averted face. Encouraged, I purred on, expressing my appreciation at the way in which she had helped in the routines of the school, had stayed out of a particularly ugly confrontation between staff and several other girls, and commented on her changed appearance.

She was sitting back in the chair now, was more full-face, and her eyes less guarded. Dare I essay an interchange of words between us by putting a question to her? Not quite yet.

"Meg and I are very pleased that you have come to our school, and we are looking forward to getting to know you over the next few months". There was a working of her facial muscles. Was that a dimple I glimpsed? "We are only afraid that you may not come back after your court appearance tomorrow, so I do hope that you will make the best of yourself to the magistrate. Could you tell him that you're sorry for whatever you did and wouldn't do it again?"

"Uh", and a nod.

"Would you mind telling me — if it is not too private — why you have to go to Court?"

The eyes continue to hold mine, the lips half-parted. The tongue flicks nervously. I do believe our new daughter is going to say her first word to me.

"Buggery" she gruffs.

Buggery? Had I heard right? The focus of my eye takes in her 15-year-old boyish, yet protrubescent, figure. No.

Was it 'Bugger off?' Look at the expression in her eyes. No.

In the milli-second in which I review and reject these possible answers to my simple question, I realise that either I must settle for incomprehension and a sympathetic nod on my part, or a bid for understanding and a step forward in our relationship.

Evelyn's eyes await my response warily.

"I'm very sorry, Eve . . . a car passed in the road . . . I didn't hear you".

"Bur-glar-y" she enunciates.

She did return to us the following day, with a suspended sentence. And, indeed, this inveterate truant stayed with us nearly into her nineteenth year. I make no claim that she benefitted, but, as shall transpire from some of the following pages, Rowen House certainly did.

An Unlikely Applicant

We had advertised in the local Job Centre for Houseparents and I had managed to deter all sorts of unlikely applicants.

This telephone call sounded the most unlikely one of all. Young girl, 20 years old, she said. Cut-glahss accent. Never had a job, she said (and my mind drifted off to have a quick wallow in its favourite prejudices. And never **had** to work, my girl, I thought. Country living, Red Setters, Volvo Estate, Ponies, a well-groomed, glistening-maned horse found in the Paddock on her 18th birthday. A Sports car with a sparkling silver grille from Daddy on her 21st, I bet. Mummy popping up to Town from time to time to make sure her clothes were in fashion, and to renew her blue-rinse. I know the type!).

"The only thing I've done since leaving school is to help Mummy with the horses". The voice chinked prettily and self-deprecatingly. (There! told you!).

"Ah, I see. Very interesting. But I'm afraid the sort of child we've got here is rather . . . rough". There was no way in which I wanted to say a word against our girls, but I wanted to put this young lady off without hurting her feelings. I told her frankly the kind of thing they might tell her to do . . . But she didn't.

"Yes well I **am** looking for a challenge".

"And I hope you find something suitable", my mind made up, "but I think you ought to look for a challenge which you have a reasonable chance of overcoming. If you misjudge the degree of challenge, you may be overwhelmed and become discouraged from attempting anything". (This career-counselling is a piece of cake. And she does sound a nice girl. She deserves a word of friendly advice).

"You say you have been helping your . . . mother with her horses. What

27

exactly does that . . . work entail?"

"Breaking them in".

"Breaking them in! You mean . . ."

"Well, just getting young horses ready for their new owners. Accustoming them to their first bridle". (My mind presented to me a vivid image of flaring nostrils, piano-keyboard teeth, bucking rear-haunches and HOOVES!). "And then you have to get close enough to get them used to having a saddle fitted, and then much later, the weight of the human body".

"Ah, I see. Very interesting. You sound as if you have had exactly the right work-experience for this school. Can I bring along some of our fillies to your place so that you can meet them and they you, and you can tell me whether you'd still like to work with us".

A few days later we wound our way along narrow lanes to arrive at a house, stables and kennels in a beautiful fold of the Derbyshire hills, which was to become a most pleasant Isle of the Aves to the girls and myself over the following years.

Sally, as pretty and trim as her voice, came out to meet us, and she and the girls took to each other instantly and forever.

I still had forebodings that Sally's mother, tweeded, broqued, and blue-rinsed, would not allow her carefully-cultured daughter to hob-nob with these, our city toe-rags.

Ann soon dispelled my fears when she emerged from the stables, scarf around her head to protect her hair, sleeves rolled up, to welcome our little party. She put aside the fork with its long curved tines, paid at least as much polite attention to the 'toe-rags' as to their headmaster. But no, she wouldn't shake hands: well, we could see why, couldn't we? And she rubbed her itching nose with the back of her hand with its carefully-separated fingers. "Well, I must go in now to take my wellies off, and wash my hands . . . Yes, 'course you can". And she briskly walked off towards the house, her puppy-dogs and a couple of our puppy-bitches yelping behind her, dropping aitches behind them as they scampered.

I stayed seated outside, basking in the sunshine, but uncomfortable in the suddenly-cold bath-wallow of my prejudices.

The Artful Dodger Lives

The psychologist had penetrating brown eyes and had done the preliminary tour of our premises without comment, almost without rejoinder.

We had arrived back in my room and I sought to allay any bad impression he may have gained from the premises by beginning to outline our plans for improving their facilities.

He interrupted me gently. "No, please let me explain what I am looking for, Mr. Purdy. I'm not looking for superior accoutrements, or furnishings, or at the fabric of the curtains. I can see you haven't been open long. This is the fourth school I have visited, and the other three schools are well-established with good reputations and, quite candidly, much better equipped than this one. But what I am looking for is a home for a very disturbed little girl — I say little: she is 12, but has the emotional age of a 4-year-old at times. She needs a home; she needs parents. She was born in Holloway prison, was rejected by her mother and taken care of by the other inmates. Several unsuccessful fostering attempts were made, before a firm fostering was effected with a childless couple. Two years later, they had their own child, and" his long sensitive fingers made an atomic-mushroom explosion, "they sent her back to the Social Services. We now need a home during the school-term until she is at least 18. During the holidays she will live in a Children's Home. And I ought to tell you that she is so disruptive that the staff threatened to give in their joint notice if we didn't move her. But I felt that she is so disturbed that it would have been disastrous for her to have to be moved yet again, and I was prepared to look for a whole new staff for the Home. But I managed to persuade them to stay".

"In that case", I replied, "it may be more truly helpful to talk with one of our girls who is in the same situation as your Nell. Kit's mother died a couple of years ago, and has had difficult experiences in a Children's Home. I'll go and fetch her".

As a result of their conversation Kit took a keen personal interest in Nell, and offered to be the one who wrote to her telling her about her new school, its situation, the other girls and herself. Nell replied, and in due course arrangements were made for her to visit the school with the personal tutor who was the only form of education felt remotely to meet the child's needs in recent months.

Kit commandeered Nell at the door and took her round the building to meet people and orient herself.

By the time she was introduced to me she looked distinctly overwhelmed by cordiality and kindness. A poor wee waif of a girl, pinched features, mouth hanging open, doffing her smile after everyone she met.

Was this the terror I had heard of? I asked her teacher, when Kit had swept the unresisting Nell off arm-in-arm.

"Yes, she's a dear girl underneath, really. I've come very close to her, as close, that is to say, as one can become to someone who's not really there, to someone who has never really developed into a person. At first I used to take her on outings to museums and suchlike, which my individual pupils who are in some sort of trouble usually enjoy. But not Nell. She just used to stare at nothing, while she clung onto my arm. And it's very difficult going around with someone hanging onto you who has no rhythm of walking with you. I gave up shopping trips for this reason, and, besides, she's such a compulsive thief that I couldn't afford to stop in front of anything which was not well protected with a glass case or she'd have it. Even when I realised that she stole, she would somehow manage to steal something in my very presence. I felt such a fool when the Home staff would tell me a day or so later that she'd been at it again.

"As far as her education goes . . . . Well, you can see by her books here not far. And what she has done has been because I've threatened not to sit next to her until she gets something down on paper. Most of the time I just sit next to her with our arms round each other. I try to unwrap her arms to get some work done, but she justs clasps tighter". Her eyes round wide and her hands flutter delicately. "Sometimes, Mr. Purdy, I can't get to go to the toilet, and I have to ask her". Think of that. The teacher asking her pupil if she can go to the toilet!

"It's wearing, but the real worry is when she hasn't got that one-to-one attention. I don't see it often, because she comes to me individually, but she can be impossible in a group of children if she doesn't get her own way. I've seen her shout and bellow at a member of staff for no reason at all, throwing things around the room, and the **lan**guage . . ."

The theme of her solo violin seemed to be taken up by a full orchestra of sound as we become aware of the rush of angry footsteps along the corridor, the door bursting open and three figures thrusting themselves hotly into the room. Following the sense of her teacher's words, I looked to Nell, the centre of the three figures, as the cause of the commotion. But her gait was shambling, her face white, her mouth open, her arms hanging nervelessly, gripped on either side by Kit and Lorna. My eyes turned to Kit as the epicentre of the disturbance.

"I'm sorry to come bargin' in 'ere like this, Bryn. And 'scuse me", to the teacher. "But me an' Lorna has got some'ink to report to yuh. Nell's bin stealin' 'cross the shop. We took her over to meet Jill an' James, 'coz they're friends of the school, sort of part of it, ain't they? Well, Jill invited us into her sitting-room, like she does sometimes, and was reely friendly towards Nell. An' when we got back to school, Nell shows us this bar of chocolate what she pinched from Jill's. We was there all the time; we dunno 'ow she could'a done it". The teacher nods sympathetically.

I rise from my chair to meet this new challenge of theft. Kit waves a flat hand towards me, "No, it's alright, Bryn. We've dealt with it".

I settle back indeterminately.

"**An**' she was **grinnin'**". Kit's voice rose, peaked in recalled indignation, and broke. "**Grinnin'**". Looking to Lorna for confirmation, "Wasn't she? Grinnin'. **We** told 'er, Lorna an' me, din't we Lorna? We told 'er you don't pinch from Jill an' James. I've pinched from shops meself, but not any more, an' not from friends".

Lorna, who usually has a mind and words of her own could only repeat, directing herself now to the poor mute Nell, "You don't pinch from Jill and James".

Nell shook her head several times, and her moving but soundless lips may have been revising the first catechism of her new tutors. "You don't pinch from Jill and James".

"Anyway, we sez to 'er, din't we, Lorna? You gotta take that back. She jus' shook 'er 'ed. She '**ad** stopped grinnin', but she just shook 'er 'ead. So we said we'd take it back for her, but she'd got to come with us. So we just turned 'er round, got 'old of an arm each, and marched 'er back acrost the shop. We waited for the shop to be empty before we told Jill what we come about. An' she took it real well, like we knew she would. She spoke very nice to Nell, told her it was wrong to steal, and that she was always welcome to come over to see her".

A pause indicated that the story was told. From their infinity-stare Nell's eyes focused on the headmaster in her quest for what would be 'done' about her theft.

"Anyway, Bryn, jus' thought you ought to know about it, tha's all. Now, Nell, let's go an' 'ave that cup of coffee I poured out for you ten minutes ago. It'll be goin' cold. Dunno how you can drink it with only 4 sugars".

The Case of the Phantom Scratcher

Kit had done well, I suppose, to contain her anger till the Moot the following morning. It was an improvement, certainly, on the sudden losses of temper, with or without pretext, and the indiscriminate vituperation with which she had favoured the community on her admission to the school twelve months before.

Sally had spent nearly an hour the previous evening with the high-bucking filly, listening to her grievance, stroking her mane — blowing up her nostrils, for all I know. But at least her fury had been coralled.

By the following morning each member of the community knew the details of Kit's grievance. I sensed from the averted eyes and tense stillness of everyone else, and Kit's folded arms, crossed thighs, and swinging foreleg, that it might be dangerous to let the Moot take its usual course.

"Since we all know why Kit is upset this morning, I wonder if it might not be as well if I were the Chairgirl this morning". No smile greeted this tired little jest, but there did seem to be an easing of the tension, and, encouraged, I went on:

"In fact, since several girls have been as distressed as Kit herself about this business, because they feel acutely under suspicion, perhaps it might be as well if I raised Kit's Moot Point myself. So, I will just run over the facts which led up to . . ."

Kit's hand had gone up simultaneously with her beginning to speak. "Point of order. 'Scuse me for interrupting, Bryn, but I think I ought to be allowed to raise **my** Moot Point in my own way. 'Scuse me an' all that".

31

The metronomic swinging of her foreleg had increased uncontrolledly and the leg bucked off her other knee. Kit made almost to stand up, then, with a great effort of containment, tucked her heels girl-like on her chair-cushion, hugged her legs and, head down, clenched her knees into the orifices of her eyes.

The emotional quotient in the room had risen sharply, more due to the quality of Kit's feeling than to the import of her words, and I began speaking to allow her to recollect herself sufficiently to talk again. "I accept your Point of Order, Kit. I only wished to appeal to people to listen with care and sympathetically to what you have to say, and not to think you're accusing them of . . . doing it. When I sat down I felt a certain resentful tension among the community: now I feel everyone wants to listen to you, Kit".

The head raised itself, the locks of hair were thrown back, the eyes stared fixedly, the locks thrown back again, this time needlessly.

"It was like this 'ere, see. That record was given me by . . . me mum . . . " We all knew how much it had cost her to make a reference to the mother who had died two years ago. She may have sensed our response, and said it again, as if not having acceded to yet another fit of lost temper had given her new strength. ". . . by me mum. And I don't think anyone should have scratched that record on the player last night after tea". She breathed out, her head dropped as she looked accusingly round at everyone as her indignation overcame her again momentarily, but she gathered herself once more and her gaze fixed itself on the door-lintel.

"And I **know** I shoon't 'ave left me record out, as Bryn's always telling us, an' I know a scratch can never be mended, but . . ." and suddenly her thought spiralled upward out of her original resentment, "I just want to know who done it . . ."

It was Meg's gentle voice that balmed the painful silence that followed.

"I would like to thank Kit for having spoken in such a dignified way, and everyone else for having listened so sympathetically. The problem here has been that Kit has become so angry when she felt a grievance in the past, and has caused such a lot of ill-feeling by openly accusing people of wronging her, that I hope she will understand how difficult it is for us to respond to her appeal".

"Well, I'll say it again, Meg: I was angry last night, and I'd like to say sorry to Susan and Jackie for talking about them, but all I want to know is who done it".

"I'd like to say sorry to Kit for talking about her to Jackie". This from Susan.

"And I'd like to propose that we buy another record for Kit because me and Susan was talking about her behind her back".

"No, that's not fair": from another: "we all ought to share buying it". General assent. The emotional tide is so high now that surely a confession will wash over the ramparts of the guilty person's resistance.

Kit again, warm, relaxed and smiling:"No, it's alright, you guys, I don't want you to spend your money. Besides its only one song that's scratched. I can listen to the rest. No, what I really want is to know who done it, like I say. I don't want to think that anyone of you girls is afraid to tell me that she scratched my record".

I applied a clumsy tourniquet to the bleeding silence.

"I very much regret that this matter has not been fully resolved this morning. I cannot see how anyone can fail to be moved by Kit's evident sincerity. Let us pass on to the next business".

Meg put an arm round Kit's shoulders and stroked her hair with her cheek.

Nell crawled across the room on her knees, slunk on to the sofa next to her and nestled close, appearing to stroke Kit's ear with her nose.

As the next business commanded my main attention, I was only marginally aware of the two girls hugging each other, rocking slightly, and Kit's affectionate whisper, "You silly little bugger".

The rest of the Moot passed at its usual foot's pace, and it was only during the coffee break that I heard some half-story about perfume. Incensed, I went hot-foot in quest of Kit. Who the hell does she think she is? If anyone round here is going to play A. S. Neill it's going to be me.

"Ah, Kit! What's this I hear?"

"Whadja mean?"

"This tale about you and Nell and some perfume".

"Oh, that! Well, you know that Nell come up to me in the Moot an tole me that it was 'er what scratched me Abba?"

"No".

"Oh, well, everyone else seems to 'ave known. Anyway she come up to me an' whispered what she done. It was an accident, an' she was very sorry. So, after the Moot, I took 'er up to me room — she was still upset, see — an give 'er a bottle of me perfume".

"You gave her a bottle of perfume after she scratched your record? . . . Where did you learn to do that?"

"Dunno. Rowen 'Ouse, I s'pose".

"I dunno either. You've never caught **me** doing tricks like that. I know a chap that did, though. Do you want to borrow my paperback copy of **Summerhill?** There's a good story on page 254".

"No, fanks. I'm not much into readin'".

The Case of the Phantom Snatcher

"It's 'appened agen".

"No!"

"It 'as. They'v pinched Nell's photo-album, with them pictures of 'er as a baby in her mother's arms".

"The BASTard . . . Wait till I catch 'em . . . 'oo can it be?"

"We just don't know, Kit. We just have to remain calm till the thief makes a false move".

"Yes, but Bryn . . ."
"Where is Nell now?"

It is a very unpleasant business. Our little community is racked by anxiety and mutual distrust. It began a week ago, when Eve's favourite **Queen** record 'went missing'.

She searched throughout the building, first distraught, then disconsolate. The raucous sound and insistent beat of that group of young men spoke to her heart. I had lent her headphones and she turned up the volume to anaesthetize some private misery, time after time, hour after hour, day in day out.

But now she was without her analgesic. She felt the pain again. Not for her the usual refuge of the child in distress. She may not have cried since infancy; she could not shout defiance; she could find no relief in tantrum. She had learnt a kind of numb stoicism.

The missing record did, however, concentrate the communal mind on Evelyn herself. Isolate, and no one's companion, we yet realised now that she was everyone's friend. Each of us recalled some dumb kindness she had offered us. When we were sad we sought out Eve and reposed in the aura of her silence, in which inhered the deeper quality of stillness. If we were upset, Eve was the nurse we allowed to cross the **cordon militaire** of our anger. She had no words to offer, but her stillness was balm.

Eve never hurt anyone. The loss of the record hurt her. Her hurt was our hurt. We returned the investment of her concern for us at compound interest, and expressed our love for her more volubly. At first discomfitted, Evelyn learnt to return smile for smile, touch for touch, handclasp for handclasp, hug for hug, kiss for kiss. Our community cohered, grew closer, by reason of the misfortune of the loss of the record — which was suddenly found, among a pile of others, just as we were beginning to forget it.

But our community was riven again by a further series of missing items. Several times a day, a girl would bewail the loss of some possession. They were mostly trumpery objects, of little value, but irritating to the body communal.

Kit expressed the irritation well one Moot: "'f anyone **wants** a half-used piece of scented soap, you're welcome, mate, but I wished you'd ask me fust". For some days we were able to lessen our annoyance by humorously referring to The Phantom Snatcher.

But the thefts continued — pencils belonging to several girls from the classroom, old slippers, and, increasingly, items of clothing from Nell — and mutual distrust infiltrated and poisoned the communal spirit. Small covens of girls gathered in private. They speculated, divined the 'culprit', and made their accusations public. The rest of the staff and Eve were having to work overtime, dousing the conflagration of accusation and extinguishing each spark of suspicion as it flared. Her growing reputation of total integrity placed Eve above suspicion, as did the high incidence of thefts from Nell place **her** beyond it. But all the others became victims in turn, randomly of theft, or by accusation. And by turn we sympathised, and examined each case. In the end all we knew was that if one girl, by circumstantial evidence, could have perpetrated **one** theft, then she had an alibi for the next. In another case, the theft of Nell's scarf, suspicion fell heavily on Laura as only she and Nell were in the building at the time, but when Nell's retracting ballpoint pen went missing, Laura was at the hairdresser's. And so on. We were baffled and humbled, and apology became the order of the day.

But then,
"It's 'appened agen . . ."
"Nell's photo album . . ."
The **Bas**tard . . ."
. . ."We just have to remain calm . . ."
"Yes, but Bryn . . ."
"Where is Nell now?"
"In the big bedroom".

Eve rose from the table, leaving her mug of tea, to meet the latest crisis, and we sped off by different routes to comfort Nell. It says much for Eve's increased confidence and professional concern that she arrived at the bedroom door at exactly the same moment as the Headmaster. We both slowed to avoid a collision before Eve, making a quick assessment of priorities, gave me the gentlest of rugby-football hand-off's — left hand firmly on my chest — and grunted "Leave 'er t' me".

I stood for several seconds in the attitude in which Eve had left me, quite still, my breathing suspended. As it were televisually, I replayed the incident of the 'hand-off' in slow motion, frame by frame, several times. In that moment the head had began to lose his authority in running his own school: and yet, not as blood ebbs from a vascular wound, but as it circulates through another part of the body politic, released from its tourniquet.

As the fire-door swung to with a thud in my face, Kit arrived hot-foot and hot tempered. I intervened between her and the door, "We'll leave Eve for a minute or two alone with her".

When we entered together, Eve was sitting next to Nell, arm round her shoulders, trying to comfort her with that gruff voice, like a crow trying to purr. Kit sat herself on the other side of Nell, the heat of her anger against the culprit melted to compassion for the victim, who sat on the bed, head-hung, fingers shredding the paper tissue which Eve had given her to mop the tears, her whole body piteously wracked by sobbing. Kit, now crying herself, tugged Nell to her, shaking the curtain of hair from side to side without disclosing her features. "Ne' mind, babe, we'll find it for yuh . . . Can I go an' get tha' favourite perfume of mine that you like so much . . . Or can I share a fag wi' 'er, Bryn? You can see she's upset".

"Naw, Bryn, can ah tek 'er to 'er room . . . ?" Eve was looking thoughtful " . . . to see if **ah** can 'elp 'er look for 'er photo-album".

"Alright, Eve: she obviously needs a lot of comforting. Now, Kit, I think you **could** do with a fag, as I feel that probably Nell is **beyond** being comforted by one. But you musn't tell anyone else. You know that I don't want people coming to me **pretending** to be upset so they can have an extra fag".

And so Eve and I led our disconsolate girls severally to their appropriate ports of comfort. Mine was the easier task, and Kit was soon restored to her cheerful cockney self.

Half an hour later, Eve knocked on my door and, hesitating momentarily while she ovecame her own communication problem, she spoke in that husky contralto which had begun to take the place of her grunt-diapason when she had something significant to say.

"Can y' come to Nell's room, Bryn. She's got summat to . . . tell yuh".

I followed Eve to the single room where Nell's gross disturbance had obliged us to place her.

Nell sat on her bed, her face still curtained by hair from her hung head, but now still in limb, apart from an occasional convulsive sob.

"Hello, Nell: Eve says you want to tell me something . . ."

But there was no need for words, as my eye caught her open suitcase which had been pulled from under her bed. The photo album lay open on top at the picture of a mother lovingly holding an infant in her arms, and beside it lay Kit's half-used piece of scented soap, fluffed now with Lorraine's second best pair of slippers, in which were neatly placed half-a-dozen pencils inscribed with different names, including Nell's. Also Nell's comb, Nell's new scarf, Nell's woollen gloves and Nell's retracting ball point pen — all items 'stolen' during the past week.

Eve had sat next to Nell, arm protectively round her shoulders, staring at me appealingly and warily, like an animal with young in the lair at the approach of a possible predator. "She didn't mean no 'arm . . ." Her voice had lost that gravelly edge and took on a new vibrance as she sought clemency for another. "She knows she done wrong. She's promised she won't do it again". Nell's face raises itself plaintively and dolefully to perceive my reactions. 'Y' won't, will y?" to Nell. "An' she's goin' to give all them things back. Aren't y'?"

Kit's infallible nose for where the action is leads her into the room behind me. After a moment's astonishment, during which she apprises herself of the situation, she sits next to Nell again, puts an arm round her shoulders, and gusts at her. "Right little tea-leaf, in'cha? Oo's the Phantom Snatcher then? Oo's pinched me photo-album? Boo-hoo".

She tugs at her and somehow shakes a smile onto Nell's face. "We saw Eve ge'in' a fuss when she lorst 'er **Queen** tape, did we? So we thought we'd **arrainge** for a few little treasures of our own to get pinched, did we?"

Nell is trying to cover her discomfiture — and her giggles — with both hands pressed to her face.

"'**Ow** many times do we aff to tell y' that if y' want more attention, you just asks your friends. An' **we**'re your friends. Aint we, Eve? An' we're goin' to att**end** to you now. An' **you'd** better ge' out, Bryn. It wouldn't be proper for Nell to be flashin' 'er slip and pants at you when we tickle 'er to deff. Ready, Eve?"

And the door thuds behind me to muffle Nell's shrieks as her fellow-communards exact retribution on her for her crimes.

An Inspector Calls

Our two visitors have spent the morning at the school, and, after a tour and a talk, are preparing to leave.

"Well, thanks for talking to us, Bryn, and showing us round".

I went back to the classroom, and Tina arrests me suspiciously.

"Oo's that feller, Bryn? 'E was askin me about 'ow I was gettin' on".

Normally I would have told her to return to her classwork, and to ask again at a more appropriate time. But perhaps it may be instructive to explain to her . . .

"As a matter of fact, Tina, 'that feller' spent a whole morning of his time just to find out how you personally are getting on. He's the man responsible for all the children in Special Schools in Derbyshire. It's not often that Special Education Officers take the trouble to visit us, but never before to ask how one girl is getting on".

Tina narrows her eyes. "Oh yeh! An' what did you tell 'im".

"I told him that, after a shaky start, during which we were offering daily prayers that you would become a school refusal, or abscond or something — or **any**thing — you are settling in very well".

"Huh", Tina turns again to her books. "Well, 'e'd better not try sendin' me back to an old-fashioned school, or I'll play up and get expelled again".

NELL : *A Correspondance Verité*

There are many expert's-eye-views of the disturbed child.

For years I had desiderated a child capable of presenting rationally the disturbed-child's-eye-view of herself. Having failed, I myself became the man-with-the-camera, recording daily events as I see them happening.

And then, one day, it happened.

Not quite as I had desiderated, and far from rationally. Disconcertingly, Nell seized the camera from me and turned it **on** me — like a rifle.

Here is the language of the disturbed — scabrous, repetitive, and ill-spelt. I transcribe the letters we wrote to each other over a period of 8 months but offer no commentary. For a season I played a restrained, soft-footing deferential Frank Doel to her rebarbative, hustling Helene Hanff, with all of the latter's vigour, if not grace, of expression. We co-existed in the same building, but an Atlantic of sympathy and language divided us. The references to summer, first made in the depths of climatic winter, followed my metaphorical explanation to her that an eventual warming of our personal relationships was as inevitable as the changing of the seasons.

Several of the letters were typewritten, as the occasional flourishes of £-signs and meaningless punctuation may indicate.

Towards other members of staff, particularly Meg and Eve, she was openly and clingingly affectionate.

To Peg Leg & Bryn   Nov.20
     Thursday £EVening
Dear Bryn,
          I got your letter [of which I retained no copy, but it seems to have included a reference to Nell's adoptive state, which she had broached in that day's Moot.] and the greeny [a boiled lime sweet].
If my sister hadn't told me they wern't my real parents I wouldn't be here now that is what i was trying to Tell you and the girls in the moot. Please don't say anything to my social worker when she comes to visit me like you said she was going to do.
        See you later Alligator (in a while
                               crocodile)
             Love Nell
P.S. Ta for greeny

To FUNNY MAN   Nov.26
Dear Mr funny man
    I dona like you
    your to funny for me

To that funny man with the beard   Nov.26
    who I call Jimmy and who wears
    specticals and who has a wife called Peg Leg

  Dear Mr Purdy
          Please may a certian young lady have some chocolate Rasins and a Greeny.
          The certian young lady is the person who has typed this letter to you
                  Yours Sincerly
                    ?

To BASTERD   Nov. 27
DEAR MR PURDY   11.30
              I HATE YOU PISING GUTS AND WILL YOU CON
TACT my cosio [social] worker so I can go to a different z school

Dear Nell,   Thursday November 27
      Thank you for your letter, which I am passing on to your social
worker.
      My love to ya, Jummy. [a reference to a Scots brogue she had
assumed latterly] . Have a chocolate raison and a greeny. [enclosed] .
                      The Funny Man

(Note found on bedroom floor of another girl)
Dear Bryn
              I am sorry for what I said in that letter   please don't show it to my
social worker, I don't really want to leave. I just wrote it because I was in a
bad mood
                                      from Nell
P.S. I Want to stay till I am eighteen if I am allowed
P.P.S. Please forgive me. (please write back)
                                      from Nell

                                      Thursday evening
Our dear Nell,
      I am glad that I had not posted the letter to your social worker — and
very glad to think we shall be friends for years to come
                      Our love
                      Meg n' Bryn
          P.S. 'Ave a greeney.

    to Bryn
dear bryn
          i hate you
                from Nell

Nell
          I LOVE YOU
                from Bryn

(Telephone call from public kiosk)
    "I still hate you even though I've got your letter"

Dear Nell,

I still love you, even though you have just made an abusive telephone call.

Bryn.

Dear Nell, Friday Nov.28 a.m.

Thanks for your letters last night and today. May I talk to you about your sister some time?

Have a greeney to take down town with you.

Love
Bryn.

Dear Bryn

Just because I dropped that Jug when I was filling it up, It doesn't mean to say I still don't hate your guts

Love from Nell

P.S. Please write back
P.P.S. I still hate your guts
P.P.P.S. Love from Nell

Dear Nell Nov.28 2o'clock

I knew you were throwing that jug on the floor to let me know you still couldn't stand me.

Did you get your suitcase [from town]. Here are a few raisins to put in it.

Love
Bryn

To Bryn Purdy Dec.1st

When you wrote that letter some time last week saying "can I talk to you about your sister" well you can. If you want to talk to me about me sister come into the sick room. In about 5 minutes. When Sally come last week I Promised her I'd ask you to ring her and see if we can go Horse Riding today

Love Nell

[grafitto found on toilet wall] January 8th

I luv my dad and nobody's going to part the basterd from me.

Bryn Purdy never cares about me cause he's a basterd.

40

Dear Nell,
   I found some writing on the toilet wall about your dad and me. Wouldn't you rather write to me directly? Here's some writing paper.
                    My love,
                          Bryn

                                   January 10th
Dear Bryn,
   Just because I am being nice to you, it does not mean I still don't hate you. And someone might have told you that last night I broke my nail file and scratched all my wrist, arms and legs. So now I still hate your pissing guts and your a basterd
                          from
                    GUESS WHO

                                   10.1.81
Dear Nell,
   Just because I spoke sharply to you when you telephoned me last night from the public call-box does not mean that I don't still love you and look forward to the time when you and I are going to be friends in the Summer.
   I hope you don't find your nail file.
   Do be careful how you go downstairs.
                    Love
                          Bryn

Dear Bryn
   I am not sorry I gave you my nail file last night because I can always go into the kitchen and get a sharp knife and slach my wrist. I've done it before and I'll do it again (I bet you never thought of me going that far)
   When I go to the Dentists on Wednesday at 9.30a.m. I would like Eve and Meg to come with me and if Eve can't come with me, I'll will not go. Oh dear me I don't know why I'm waste my lead and my time on a silly Basterd, Wanker, Get, Count, Tosser like you for
                    from guess
                          WHO?

                                   January 12th
Dear Nell,
   Let me tell you why you waste your lead and your time on a silly bastard like me. Because you want to test me out and find out if I **really**

care for you or whether I am only saying I do. *I* know I care for you and am patient enough to wait till we are true friends, one with another. It might happen any day now, or it may take some weeks or even a few months. But I feel confident that it will have happened by the Summer.

You are a wise girl to test me out so thoroughly.

Love
Bryn

Telephone call   January 13th

"I 'ate you, yuh bastard. I hate yuh".

January 13th

Dear Nell,

I realised you were worried about your Dad when you told a lie about his death, so I asked [the psychologist] if he would come and see you to tell you what he knows. We have arranged for him to come on Thursday.

We still love you

from

Meg and

The Man you Love to Hate

Dear Bryn,

I don't know why every time I want to talk you you start talking about my Past. I don't mind but every time you talk to me about my Past I want to hate you more. but we can't live together without talking to each other so that's why I am still talking to you. I still hate your guts.

from

Nell

Dear Nell,   14 January

I do understand how upset you feel when you think about and hear me talk about your damaging past and I promise I will talk more about the happier future which I believe you will have.

So I will keep saying:

"See you in the Summer"

Love
Bryn.

,;;;⅞uyi kglflppp
y

Dear Mr. Purdy
        I still hate your Bloody guts I think that your a Fucking Basterd
        And if you think you can keep me in every night for the rest of
term then you are thinking wrong. Last week you TRIED to keep me and
Sonia in but we still went out, so you cant keep me in againn you Basterd
                                Yours Hatefully
                                        Nell
P.S. I still hat e your pising guts (your a basterd)
P.S.S. Get the message
P.S.S.S. (your a basterd, wanker, tosser)
P.S.S.S.S. The only reason why i dont call you names when Megs there is
                because I dont want to upset her

Dear Nell,
                Our love
                        Meg and Bryn

Dear Bryn
        I hate you
        I think your a basterd
                        Love from
                                Nell

Dear Bryn
        Iam sorry But I don't know way I hate you so much (BUT I
STILL FUCKING DO) and as I waz writeing this letter I lit a Dopper up
with some matches and if you want to see me about the matches I'm in my
bedroom
                                Yours hatefully
                                        Nell
P.S. I still hate your guts

Dear Nell,
                Thanks for your letter and your love.
                I enclose some paper
                                        Love
                                                Bryn

Dear Bryn

Just because I am talking nicely to you it does not mean I still don't hate you pising guts. your a Basterd and if you want to you can tell Eve (but nobby else) about my dad and my Past But you Better not tell anybody else

From
Nell

P.S. You won't stop me from hitting Shelley tomorrow

Dear Nell,   January 20th 4O'clock

Just because I'm going off duty now to go home doesnt mean that I haven't enjoyed your company today. Thanks for going to the bank with me.

Have **you** talked to Eve about your Past?

Love
, Bryn

P.S. I cant stop you hitting Shelley but I will stop Fred coming in to school.

Dear Bryn

When I was at home I keeped haveing Dreams about my dad dying and when I came back to school I knew that if I told you my Dad is died, that you would try to find out if he is died and if he is not died so I made up a lie Just to see if you would find out for me

Love Nell

P.S. I still Hate your pising Guts

Before I do any jobs for you I want a fag. and if you get me in a bad mood tonight I will run away again

Love
Nell

Dear Nell,

I never give a fag to anyone who demands one

If you do run away, which is easy to do, then you will not watch late TV tonight and will have to stay in your room some time tomorrow

Love
The Man you Love to Hate

Dear Bryn

Your only doing that so I wont get onto Shelley for flirting around Fred but I will still find a way of belting the fat cow and she can tell you what I said to her when he said R—— would have sex and I will tell her to tell you

from
Nell

January 15th

Dear Bryn

I hate your guts. Just because I am talking to you it does not mean I don't still hate you. Your a basterd, wanker and I know a name you don't like

"HI FUNGUSFACE"

From
Nell

P.S. and don't put "from the man you love to hate" at the bottom of your letters

Put "?" or "Bryn"

Dear Nell,

See you in the Summer time

Love
Fungus Face

[written on parcel paper]   Dear Bryn   I hate your pising guts, your a Basterd

Please put your letter repling back in my room in about 5 or 10 mins.

Nell

1.45p.m.

Dear Nell,

Thank you for your letter

I'm very sorry for the delay in replying. I thought that the piece of brown paper was waste.

I enclose some paper for your next couple of letters

PLEASE WRITE SOON

Love
Bryn

[Letter in a different hand]
Nell wants to see her foster parents Nell says she calls them mum and dad.
Nell cannot remember her real father as such
They adopted her
and changed her name to S——
EVE

January 21st '81
Dear Nell
Thank you for telling me about the old man who molested you.
I'm sorry I had to use force to bring you back into school this evening after you had run out. When you said that you insisted on going out in the dark to look for Fred, I had to bring you in for your own safety.
Love from Bryn

Dear Bryn [in a different hand again]
I have never been hit like you did me since my dad hit me
Lorraine is writing this letter for me I am sorry for absconding like that but, I was upset because Fred was not allowed in tonight. Will you please write back but don't put 'My love Bryn'. You owe me two letters
Please write back
from Nell

January 21st
Dear Nell,
I didnt hit you. I got hold of you by the arm to bring you inside. I'm sorry if it hurt, but I did offer you the choice of walking in yourself, and you said you were going to look for Fred.
I understand why you absconded, but I may have to stop Fred coming in if he upsets you like this
Bryn

Dear Bryn
Did you say That I had to stay in your office from 6 o clock up till my bedtime at 9 o clock. I will if you said I had to, you won't keep me in for long in your office I can always climb out of your office window and go and find Eve or Fred or go down and see Edith and Frank [Meg's parents] . It is now quarter past 6 so when you come for the staff meeting at about 7 o'clock well I will only be in your office for 2 instead of 3 hours. Please write back, soon, you already owe me 2 letters, 1 from this morning and now this one.

any way I dont know why I am wasting my ink and paper and time on a silly Basterd like you. and if you want to talk to me about this letter you will have to talk to me before the staff meeting

Love from Nell

P.S. I asked you if I could go home for the weekend because if I do I am going to stay there because you can only fight the dirty way your a basterd

An Induced Lull

I do apologise for exposing any civilians among you, unused to being under fire, to the unrelievedly torrid warfare of the last nine pages. What was for me sporadic sniping over a 2-month period, has become for the reader the machine gun's rapid rattle. It isn't my intention to risk language-shock to you, so let us arrange a leave.

We have heard the donkeys braying at the battle front. How go things behind the lines? How are the lions conducting their affairs back at H.Q.? During your furlough I shall tell you a tale of senior administrative folk.

An Inspector Palls

I'm afraid you'll find me here too, having doffed my infantryman's helmet and donned my officer's cap. Our little Field Dressing-Station is awaiting inspection by a top brass.

His secretary had arranged the visit. He arrived early afternoon. This was, he explained, the first special school he had ever visited. He had been made redundant in a recent reorganisation of schools, and had been redeployed as the officer in charge of secondary and special schools for his Authority. The Principal Psychologist had commended ours as a model of good practices employed in special schools. He admitted complete ignorance of the education of maladjusted children and begged to be informed about the differences between Ordinary and Special Schools. I warmed to his candour and humility, and, with this expression of mutual appreciation echoing in our ears, our relationship had a most propitious start. He quickly apprehended that our community was on first-name terms and asked whether he might reciprocate. Splendid! John and Bryn it was. The mutual rapture of our growing acquaintance seemed to expand to new dimensions when he gripped his tie, asking whether he were not thus inappropriately dressed in such an informal and friendly community. He declared himself ready to divest himself there and then of this symbol of normal professional attire. I reassured him that he was welcome to dress himself how he pleased amongst us. He mingled among the other members of the community in a friendly and unaffected manner for a further hour and took his leave of me with fulsome expressions of appreciation for his introduction to Special Education.

A day or so later John's secretary telephoned me.

"Mr. B— has asked me to tell you that Nell must be transferred to the local High School".

I am accustomed to the unexpected in the behaviour of our pupils, but admit being quite taken aback by this intelligence.

"But . . . I don't understand. Why?

"I was only told to pass on the message".

"But why? Are you sure you've got the message right?"

My discourtesy nettled an indiscretion out of this customarily most diplomatic of secretaries.

"He doesn't think Nell is receiving a proper education. I mean, you'll have to ask him yourself. All I know is that he wants Nell Lawson to move to the local Secondary School".

"Yes, I understand what you say, but Nell couldn't **poss**ibly . . . I mean . . . I don't think that Nell would find it easy to respond to the day-to-day rigours of even the most well-disposed and pastorally-oriented of Ordinary, as distinct from Special, schools".

"There is a letter for you in the Post from Mr. P— confirming what Mr. B— has asked me to tell you. Good-bye".

Silly woman! She must have got John's message wrong. Let's wait for the letter to clear up this irritating matter.

The letter did arrive. And she wasn't. And she hadn't. Nell was to be moved into an ordinary school during the next few months . . . Yes, yes, I know. Told the lady myself, didn't I? . . . Well, read the letter for yourself then if you don't believe me. But don't forget you've met Nell through her letters, and John has only met her briefly in person, the normal, friendly, intelligent kid she seems to be now.

It was one of those circumlocutory letters, dictated by one man, typed by his secretary, and signed by the Director of Education.

> . . . The Authority attaches considerable importance to securing Nell's return to full-time schooling as soon as possible. I understand that it is your intention to work to promote Nell's admission to the High School from the commencement of the Spring term and this is welcome. If you are successful in this respect I am sure that we will be able to agree a suitable revision of fees and I am happy to leave such matters to be resolved after rather than before the event.

> In fairness to you however, I should point out that if it does not prove possible to secure Nell's admission to the High School, then you should treat this letter as notification of the Authority's intention to withdraw Nell.

With the noise of the all-too-near guns at the Front in my ears, I retired behind the lines again, and primed a triple fusillade in riposte: from myself as administrator, from myself as headteacher, and from my self.

Let's hear from the administrator.

I write in response to your letter of October 5th, in which you notify me of your Authority's intention to withdraw Nell Lawson if I do not "secure her return to full-time schooling".

Few residential schools for maladjusted children — because of their situation in the remote countryside, if for no other reason — offer transfer of their pupils to Ordinary School. (I lay claim to special knowledge about this subject, as a member of the Consultative Committee of the Schools Council Working Paper 65, **Education of Disturbed Pupils** (1980). My own total commitment to the principle of integration of maladjusted pupils into Ordinary schooling began with my first headship in 1967 — 10 years pre-Warnock. When I opened Rowen House School in 1979 I chose its situation because of its potentiality for integrating our pupils into the local community and schools. The D.E.S. advised me at the time that it was the single such school in a residential area in the whole of England and Wales.

Notwithstanding the context of my beliefs and experience, I can offer no such undertaking as your letter requires in the case of such a disturbed child as Nell Lawson. In fairness, I offer no preparation, or "weaning-off" of Nell in the event of her withdrawal. We accepted the highly disruptive six-month consequences of her admission to the school, but, for the sake of the community, must require that she shall be withdrawn on the very day when that intimation of her leaving shall reach her mind.

I write this letter as the administrator of Rowen House, and it should be read in conjunction with the accompanying letter written as Head Teacher.

And now the Head Teacher.

. . . When your Principal Psychologist, Mr. M— interviewed me about a place for Nell Lawson, he indicated to me that her prime need was for a community which would offset the emotional devastation of her family's rejection of her and of several previous failed placements. Because of the depth of her disturbance, Mr. M- went so far as to request that the school might be prepared to offer care for that 12-year-old girl beyond statutory school-leaving age, until she was 18. This was the one condition mentioned by your Authority's representative, and return to Ordinary School formed no part of our contract . . .

I consider that it would be professionally inept of me to essay her "return to full-time schooling", and it would be personally deeply repugnant to add yet another failure to Nell's record.

49

While it is my broad "intention", discussed with Mr. M—, to integrate Nell into Ordinary School in the long-term, no undertaking can be offered as to its timing, and full-time schooling must remain a desirable but imponderable aim.

I have always believed that Mr. M— selected Rowen House because of . . .

dee-dah, dee-dah. Don't some headteachers go **on!** Like those frogs who inflate their throats to twice their own size when threatened. I'll be glad to get back to the Front.

So let's have a look at the third letter, a short one, which went into the same envelope addressed to the Education Officer.

Dear John,

. . . We regarded you as a very sympathetic visitor to our school, and, while I invite your Authority to review its relationship with Rowen House, may I, through the medium of this letter, make the invitation a more personal one to you to have further discussions either in person or on the telephone.

Yours sincerely,

Bryn

It may have seemed to the Administrator and the Headteacher a very impressive, double-barrelled bang, but it landed without detonating, muffled into the filing cabinet of the Special Needs Room of the Education Office. My letters proved to be the passing-bells of John's and my relationship, professional, administrative or personal. Not a line of his writing have I . . .

For the time being, however, Nell was allowed to stay with us. Perhaps Mr. M— was able to persuade Mr. P—, through Mr. B—, how difficult it is to find a place for such young people as Nell.

What's that I hear? The shrill, demented choirs of wailing grils. Furlough's over, lads. Bugle's calling. Over the top!

January 22nd

Dear Nell,

Sorry I failed to reply to your earlier letter today but so many people seemed to be coming to have a cry in my room this afternoon

I havent heard that you have run out this evening, so we can invite Fred in tomorrow, can't we?

Bryn

Dear Bryn,

Just because I am speaking nicely to you does not mean I still don't hate you. And if you tell Mr. — —, my social worker and my Aunty I will get up to my old tricks again (scratching records, picking on Shelley more often

Nell

Dear Mr Purdy
    You wanted a nice letter from me, so you've got one. I do not like you and I do not like your guts
                        from
                            Nell
P.S. (No swearing, neat and polite and only one mistake. and even full stops and commers and capital Letters).
P.P.S. Can I have another greeny D A R L I N G

Dear Bryn   24.1.81.
    I am sorry for all the nauty things I have done wile I have been at this school like Running away, fighting, swaring at you and the other staff.
    And please promise me one thing, that you won't show my social worker, Mr. —, or my Aunty [children's Home Supervisor] that letter I wrote to you yesterday.
    from when I am writing this letter until I leave this school I will try to turn over a new leaf (you didn't have to wait till the summer).
    You can show this letter to the other girls in the moot this morning along with my other letter from yesterday if you like to.
                    Love
                        from
                            Nell
                                x x x

Dear Bryn,
    When I said last night that I was sorry I bet you know that I didn't mean it. I never had a chance to hit Michelle last night so I will be going for her Today. Thanks to you I didn't get to sleep Last night till 2.30a.m. becaurs I was thinking of leaving this school. So you better not do any more Dirty fighting again. (on me)
                            Nell
P.S. I'm in no mood for a fat cow like Shelley and a fucking Bastard
                                        like you.

Dear Bryn
    It is non of your Bisness if I have sex or not, So you can keep your Big nose out of my life or else. Your not my Dad or Gaurdian — Mr. R. is my Dad and my Aunty is my guardian so you have no right whatsoever to say whether I can have sex or not. I don't tell you to go to the Bloody Loo or not so you don't tell me whether to have sex or not
                            Nell
P.S. I have taken the Pictures down off my wall because you said I had to
                    ask Tilly

51

Dear Nell   23rd January
          This is my letter for the one I didn't write yesterday
          I hope you enjoy having Fred in school tonight
          Be a happy girl.
                                        Bryn

Dear Bryn
          Please let Fred in tomorrow night. Phyllis says that Don says
he will bring him Down tomorrow night. And I am not showing off to Julie
because Julie nows what I am like because I first met Julie at [my Remand
Home]
                              Love from
                                        Nell
P.S. I truly *am sorry*
                         Love
                              from
                                   Nell
P.P.S. Please write back. you owe me 3 letters from today.

                                   26/1   11.00a.m.
          Please may I use the typewriter
          P.S. I will bring it back
          P.P.S. TA Jimmy

Dear Bryn
          Last night me and Fred were laying down on the Judo mats and
          Fred was trying to unfasten my Bra Strap and I am going to let
          him unfasten it on Wednesday night but on Wednesday night I
          will have my front fastening Bra on and I'm not bothered if you
          are on Dutie on Wednesday night. I'm still going to let him
                    (it is even on Tape)
                                   Nell
          P.S. And if you dont let him in on
                    Wednesday you'll get a cract in the mouth.

Dear Meg and Bryn   28.1
          I am sorry for running away last night.
                         Love from
                                   Nell
          P.S. Please read it in the moot.

52

I AM GOING TO BELT SHELLY — (FAT BITCH IF SHE
DOES NOT PUT THE CUPBOARD RIGHT IN MY BEDROOM
I **STILL** HATE YOUR PISING GUT'S. I HAVE STARTED
MY OLD TRICKS AGAIN
YOURS HATEFULLY
P.S. Nell

I wasn't going to ring my Aunty up realy.
I was going to ring **my** Dad up
Love
Nell

To the Man I love to Hate   15.
12.2.81.

Dear Bryn
Your are going to be sorry I ever came to this school I am not
serprised that the new girl did not stay. Because when I ring my Auntie up I
am going to ask her if I can stay home & I am going to tell her what you did
to Loriane and that you nearly broke my arm and I am going to tell her
every thing and I might have told Margret that I am not coming back after
the 2 weeks well I am only to see Fred, Kit, Eve, and nobody else
I HATE YOUR GUTS
Nell

early March '81

Dear Bryn
I was going to hit Michelle when she said I shoodl'nt smoke.
When M and I was down in the L.room I said to her "if 'I'm not allowed to
smoke then your not and she replayed "I am 14 and it is alright to smoke at
14" and I said "it is not" so I had a go at her
please write back
NR

12.3.81.

To fungus face
Dear Bryn
I might be talking nicely to you but I am not your
friend, because you will not give me any Greenys, chocolate raisins or
ordinary raisins. So if you want to be friends with me then you had better
give me some Spags [sweets]
You have not xxx given me one letter from you all term so
you had better start now
Please wright back soon or else
Yours sincerely
Nell

Dear Nell
Glad we're in touch by letter.
Choc nuts and greeney enclosed.
                    Love
                         Bryn

                                                    17.3.81
Dear Nell
        What's the point of writing to each other if you still hate my
pissing guts, and if we're never going to be friends?
                                        Luv
                                             Bryn

                                                    17.3.81
Dear Bryn
        I hate your pising guts and i most probably allways will and i will
        not be seeing you in the Summer Time, so there. Because i
        might not be here then to be friends with you
                                        Yours sincerly
                                                  Nell

                                                    19.3.81
Dear Nell,
        I do understand how you felt yesterday afternoon, and so glad
you were calm and sensible enough not to run out after Kit
        I'm sorry you are sad now
                                        Luv
                                             B

TO MY FRIEND   26.3.81.
Dear Bryn
        I would like to talk to you about my Dad sometime today.
Because I am getting a bit wrued about him again. My doctor, gave me
some Pills to ease me off a bit. and they settled me down a bit and they
also calmed me down. and when i was taking them i never got Bithcy or
Ratie as much with anybody.
                        I AM YOUR FRIEND
                Love from Nell
P.S. PLEASE WRITE BACK.

29.3.81.

Dear Nell,

It's a real pleasure to write you a letter knowing that we are friends at long last.

The Summer was a long time coming, but it was well worth waiting for.

Love
Bryn

Dear Bryn

I have now started to be happy at school so I am going to be good here at school. I think that Kit has sort of got it in for me. Please may I talk to you about her.

Please write back
Nell

— and **don't** touch my jacket.

30.3.81.

Dear Bryn

As I went through the Piano Room, Kit said to me "Nell are you jeolous that I have got the same skirt as you" and I said "No I am not, it is up to you whether you have the same skirt as me, because it is you that's wearing it" and Kit said "I dont believe you, from 5 seconds from now till you tell me the truth, you need'nt speak to me at all. And I feel as I want to burst in tears. so will you tell Kit in private that I was jealous when I heard her had the same skirt as me, but I am not anymore.

Love
Nell

P.S. Could you please ask Kit if I may have my new **jeans** back
You may read her
this letter in private.

Dear Bryn,

Your are going the right way about it, to split me and Fred up and if you do, I am not going to come back at Easter and I will do more then kill you I will personly paralize you for life, even if you do hurt sometimes, but if you split us up I will bloody parilize you for life and I **mean** that.

from Nell

P.S. and if my Social worker does come tomorrow and she sayes one wrong word I will atomatically walk out

Dear Bryn
        I hate your pising guts, your a Basterd, Tosser, wanker, cunt.
                                Nell

To my friend.
Dear Bryn
        Please don't split me and Fred up, cause you know I wouldn't
want to lose him. The reason I was crying last night was because I was
worried for Evelyn. About fifteen minuetes after you went out, I was
standing by my bedroom door fully dressed cause I was going to run out
but then I thout of the consicwenses and I knew that I'd have more fags
taken off my list and I wouldn't have been able to see Fred for friday Night
and over the Weekend so in the end I didnot run away.
P.S. Plesse could you tell me if my Social Worker is coming today or next
        week so that I can tiredy my bedroom up a bit more
P.P.S. I am your friend
                                Love
                                    from
                                        Nell
P.P.P.S. We are at the summer

                                                    4,5,81.
Dear Warwick [House parent]
        Dont send the coppers or Eve or Kit as I will run away from
coppers and Eve and Kit hate me. I will tell you the reason when Bryn
or . . . . Brings me back to school.
                                Nell
P.S. Thanks a million

Dear Mr and Mrs Purdy
                        I am coming back after the 2 weeks holiday. But
I am only coming back to see Eve, Kit, and Fred but not anybody else. Not
even you or your wife Meg.
                                Yours sincerly
                                Nell R
P.S. I am still your friend.

                                                14th May
Dear Neil [Counsellor]
        I am very sorry for telling you a lie because when you said "Are
you fantasing or did you really take Julies money". I said I did take it
because I got blamed for going into Kit's drawer and then I got blamed for
using Lorraines Make-Up, so I know I would get blamed for stealing Julie's
money. But I didn't go in Kit'es drawer nor did I go in Lorraines Bedroom
to use her Make-Up
                                Love Nell

                                                      18th May
Dear Neil
        Please may I talk to you Privatly about something that is making
me really upset. Thank you
                                        Nell

                                                      May '81
Dear Bryn
        I think we are at the summer time As i siad befor you havent seen
my worst yet
                                Love Nell

To Bryn   June 15th
        I hate your pising guts
                        your a basterd
                                        Nell

        I still love you and I always will
                                Love Nell

Dear Bryn
        I am not talking to Shelly and if I do not speak to her she gives
me a dirty look and if she keeps it up I will get up and smack her.
So you had

                                                      June 29th '81
Dear Nell,
        I've not had a letter from you for a long time — though several
you have started to write to me have been handed in (and found days later
in the toilet) — and I thought I'd write to tell you how pleased I am that the
Summer has arrived.
                                Love Bryn

                                                      July 4th '81
Dear Bryn
        Please will you tell me what you, my social worker and Eve were
talking about and what has been decided
                                ALL MY LOVE

Dear Bryn,

I'm sorry for having a go at Angela and I'm sorry for swearing at you. Please may I meet the Boys tonight

from Nell

P.S. I'm sorry
P.S.S. Please write back
P.S.S.S. You owe me 2 letters

Love from Nell

July 4th

FIRST LETTER

Dear Bryn,

Am I right thinking that Mark is allowed in on Wednesday night or Monday night. Please Put me right and which night is he allowed in on please write back to both of these letters.

All my love Nell

Dear Bryn

I do know a place where I can go for the Sommer holidays, I have been there many times But I think If I was to go there I would have to be on my best behavior and the place would have to agree and Social Services would have to agree. And also **you** would have to agree to me going there

(overleaf)   **LETTER 2**   All my love Nell

Please do not look at the third one
until you have finish the first one
God bless you (and meg,

John, Julia and Penny)

P.S. Please reply before you go home tonight
P.S.S. I do hope you will let me go to Rhondas, Goeffs and Annes, Rebeccas All my love Nell

[Nell's reference to 'a place . . . I have been many times' requires an explanation. Ronda, an Infant-trained teacher had applied to us for a post as Play Group Supervisor, which had just been filled. Not wishing to waste her talents and warmth of manner, we appointed her to a vacancy which did not exist on the staff of the school. From her growing relationship with the girls she — and her husband, Geoff, a Telecom engineer — 'befriended' several over the following twelve months, offering each one the hospitality of their home. We were all concerned about how Nell would cope with the long Summer vacation. So Ronda agreed to befriend her with this hazard in mind. Nell spent evenings with her, then afternoons for tuition and to help with the shopping, and, eventually, she telephoned one evening to ask me whether she might stay there overnight. She was effusively grateful for my consent — to an arrangement which I had already planned with Ronda. If she had known of such a plan from the outset, she might have resisted it strenuously, but because it was 'her' idea . . .]

July

Dear Nell,

Thank you very much for your letters you wrote to me the other day which I have been too busy, with visitors and Meg being away, to answer so I am asking Wyn to type it for me.

Letter 1.   Your social worker and Eve were not making "decisions" about you but were two people who care for you a lot and I wanted her to meet Eve.

Letter 2.   As I have told you I saw Mark at the Fair and he says that he is too busy with his Evening Classes to go out with girls at the moment. Also, I am not sure that the people who are responsible for you should allow you, in your present state of distress, to go out with a boy so much older than you, if we are to act responsibly.

Letter 3.   I am most pleased to answer this letter and to tell you that Ronda and Geoff have invited you to their home for the first week of the holidays.

You know how highly I think of you and I could not speak more highly of Ronda than to say to you, after all your years of unrest, that you deserve her.

Love, Bryn.

And so it was that the correspondence between Nell and me ceased. (Or rather, this episode ceased. She continues to correspond with us over the years — the last time, as I write, a few weeks ago, Christmas 1986, sending us a photograph of herself and her new-born baby).

It has been seen that she was beginning to write to Neil. I had served her need. The formality of a type-written letter may have been the catalyst which caused her to desist. A more normally affectionate relationship had supervened the old antagonism, and it was no longer necessary to write.

My last words to Nell permit me to go beyond the strict bounds of our correspondence, and describe how she did go to the home of Geoff and Ronda and their two little girls.

It will be recalled in **The Artful Dodger Lives** how Nell had caused all the professional staff of a Children's Home to threaten to resign 12 months before, and it was only with great trepidation that the Social Services

Department consented to the experimental week. Ronda and Geoff were almost carelessly sanguine, but then they were only amateurs. For my part, I knew I would be at home during that week and could arrive to relieve any contingent crisis within 8 measured minutes. The Social Services Department undertook to send down a driver and an escort to collect Nell in any emergency, day or night.

At the end of term, I delivered Nell into Ronda's welcoming arms. (And it is to be understood that, with so emotion-starved a child as Nell, this is no mere form of words. Ronda's only 'complaint' so far was that she sometimes could not prepare a meal because she was kept standing for many minutes at a time and repeatedly, clasped in Nell's arms).

For two or three days I did not move outside the earshot of the telephone, and, once, so sure that I would be needed as 'cavalry' to relieve the besieged homestead of these amateurs, I actually picked up the phone to see whether it were still working.

On the fourth day I called to see Ronda and Geoff — was **their** phone working? — and found a gentle-voiced and beatifically-smiling Nell reading a story to 3-year-old Rebecca. The only child behavioural difficulty I encountered was the impatience of a small, blond-haired moppet at having her story interrupted by this ponderously-toned and bearded intruder. I did not consider Rebecca to be part of my professional brief, and took my leave.

On my way home I marvelled how these Befrienders — these 'amateurs' — had easefully wrought a change in the state of mind of this erstwhile deeply disturbed child within a matter of days which we committed professionals had failed to effect during many strenuous months.

In a broader context, my reflections about Nell's sojourn with Ronda led to the Befriending Scheme, an idea which radically altered the operation of the school.

Must tell you about it sometime.

For the time being, arrangements were made towards the end of the week for Nell to stay into a second week . . . then a third . . . until Ronda simply invited the Social Services to allow Nell to spend the Summer holidays with them.

Summer had arrived for Nell herself, as it had for her and my relationship.

Runaways

Absconding is a canker which infests residential establishments for the unstable from time to time. During one such episode, our Evelyn, like another Luther at the church of Wittenberg, nailed — or, rather, sellotaped — her declaration of protest to the door of the Common Room.

Rowen House School is a school for girls, and the reason I am writing this is because some of them are runaways. In this school there are 11 girls. Rowen House has been open for 2½ years and most of the girls like it.

Some of them lately get fed up, and they have to go out, or, as some of us call it, running away. And that is when the police are called in and asked to look for them. It is very wrong to do this. It is very dangerous for those who walk out during the night. But I do think that they do not know the reasons why. People who run away from homes or schools do not know what danger they are in.

Those who run away only think of themselves, and not about the people who care about them and go out looking for them. The police come round asking things like what they look like and what they are wearing. Some girls I think make it bad for themselves. Say they run away about 7 o'clock and don't come in until say about half past two in the morning. The people who own the school don't have any sleep, the police don't get any sleep, and then it all happens.

The girls who are left in the school help those who run away. Everybody does what they think is right. Even the outsiders help those who run away. But the girls just take no notice of what we say to them. For them it's OK. What we say goes in one ear and out of the other. We talk for hours with them and say "Don't go out again", but do they stay in? No, they still go out into the world where it's dangerous at night. Anything could happen to them and we would be sitting in the school wondering what on earth has happened to you, or what is happening.

Sometimes in school it is like a happy family. No one walks out on us all. There might be an argument between two people, then one of the staff will ask them to go to their rooms for a while. After that, they will come down. They have got something inside them that makes them want to go out, or there might be a fight going on between two girls, and say two people who have nothing to do with it walk out. It is only yourself that lets you down. I get fed up with it, but I do not go out for hours on end so the police have to come looking for me. I just stay in, listening to records.

So you girls, take it from all of us, stay in and you will not be in danger.

61

By the Grace of . . . Providence?

Many the time we had suggested to one or another troubled child during the day, "Go and help Pat". And, tearful and still snuffling, clutching a damp and crushed tissue under white knuckles, the girl would go and 'help Pat'. She would stand about in the middle of the kitchen declaiming her woes while Pat weaved around her to and from working surface, sink and cooker.

There was a balm about her busy presence which had often tempted me too to 'go and help Pat'. Bruised from the latest affray, I would stand around and talk. Never ceasing to peel potatoes, chop onions, and stir the stew, yet she did not discontinue the frequent eye-contact which is the mark of the good listener. She was happy to follow the conversations of others without diverting them into her own channels. Always ready to see the humorous side of things and gently join the communal laughter, she never disturbed the even tenor of the conversation by making jokes herself.

There was another, more reflective, side to Pat, our first cook, before she became houseparent, teacher and counsellor. She was uncertificated in any of these professions, yet richly qualified to perform them by her personal qualities. Wife of a lay preacher whom she had met at Bible College, member of the local Methodist Church — not so much a pillar as an essence — mother of two young children, and co-teacher with her husband of a junior Bible-study class, she held deeply-felt views on the important issues of life.

She expressed her beliefs in her self rather than in words — unless you asked her, when she would respond to your question rather than see it as an opportunity for a sermon. Having enjoyed her hospitality at home with her family, I knew that the ceremony of grace was performed before and after every meal. Did she not miss it each day at school, where it had been she who prepared the meal?

"I never fail to say it", she replied, "but no one can hear me".

As the months of our colleagueship matured into friendship, I realised that her sense of humour could extend itself into her beliefs.

"I can understand why your Lord would order **your** life, Pat, in response to your prayers and your faith in Him, but why does he look after **me** so well? He sent you to this community to fulfil His will, but, from my point of view, what good luck, or Providence, brought you to work in the kitchen here? I didn't offer up a single petition. You just arrived — a gift as from Heaven, I agree, but why to **me**?"

No dispute, only smiles, ensued. In Robert Owen's words, we remained divided in opinion, but united in heart. Her faith in God's active oversight of the Universe knew no tremor in the face of my continual wonderment at the ways in which a godless Providence seemed to care for the life of our community. Daily and hourly problems would arise, be confronted, and be resolved by the forbearance, good-heartedness and skill of the **staff**. But occasional problems would arise which admitted of no professional intervention. On such occasions I could not have predicated a solution if I had ultra-human powers. And then the problem resolved itself! Time and again, by totally unforeseeable agencies! After witnessing such acts of Grace in our daily life, I would hie me first to the kitchen. "Hey, what do you think of this, Pat? You remember I told you the other day? . . . Well, after a staff meeting we decided that we were helpless . . . And then . . . And now she's up in my room, with Eve's arms around her, alternately laughing and crying . . . I could never have imagined . . . **It's** happened again! Providence rules O.K.!"

A peeled potato was dunked under the running tap and plopped into the saucepan, and Pat's expression of pleasure at the resolution of the problem offered no discouragement to my childish faith in a benign but undirected universe.

It had been an agreeable morning altogether, really. Friendly atmosphere. Nice dull moot, no fireworks, no hot potatoes for me to handle, one or two girls drifting off to start classwork by themselves before the rest of us dispersed. A perambulation. All settled. Time for me to call into the kitchen for a Pat-chat. Time to expatiate with the Cook on the imponderables of life.

I watched the apple-peel dance and spiral out of her deft fingers to lie in a shapeless and browning heap on the cutting-board. Whence did our community draw for whatever strength it possesses? I wanted to know. Surely there could be no singlemindedness in an enterprise which originated in the strength of purposeful thought of a Christian Scientist, which is lovingly administered by a practising Roman Catholic, and which has its daily bread baked, metaphorically speaking, by a devout Methodist. This is ecumenism gone mad!

The chopped apples lay white under water, gently coming to the bubble, and long slivers of carrot-peel leapt from the skilled blade.

"And what with you as cook, with Sylvia as teacher, with Alison as houseparent, and with Lesley as Befriender, this blasted community — oh sorry, this **blessed** community — wouldn't function at all without the Methodist Church". I popped a piece of freshly-diced carrot into my mouth, and continued ruminatively, "Even Neil is the issue of a good pew-serving Methodist home. You're none of you the kind of people — freely appointed by me in each case, I know, as the best person for the job — that I had thought would come and work with **me,** an arrant freethinker".

The rush of domino-falling carrot-slices on the cutting-board paused only momentarily for Pat to turn and eye me smilingly and to crack, or rather, prise open gently, the only joke I ever heard her make in over 6 years of friendship, as she loosed on me her single barbless arrow of counter-argument.

"Did you say **arr**ant, Bryn, or **err**ant freethinker?"

Guarding a Confidence

Kit and I sat in the front of the mobile classroom on the way back from an afternoon's horse-riding with Sally and Ann.

Sonya was sitting behind us and joining in the chatter with the other girls. Kit took the opportunity to have a confidential chat about Sonya's welfare.

"Don't think I'm grassin' on 'er, Bryn, but ever since that incident over Carla I know I can trust you not to put your foot in it and tell 'er what I'm tellin' you. I don't know what you can do, but I think you ought to know. You're not to tell anyone, not **any**one, Bryn. Do you understand?" A long pause. "'Cep' Meg, 'f course. Not that she asked me not to tell, but she thinks I'm one of the girls still — an' I am, but it'll lead to trouble for 'er. I've tried to put it out me mind, but I gotta tell you". All this had been conducted in a tense undertone, a volume of speech that didn't come easily to Kit, the thread of the story being barely intelligible above the rise-and-fall of chatter and laughter behind. At one point her voice rose both in indignation and in order to be audible above a sustained decibel-rise to the rear.

"Whassat? Whassat?" Sonya's voice, suspicious.

"Wadya mean?"

"I 'eard yuh say me name". A distinct edge now.

"No we didn't, did we, Bryn?"

I paid suddenly-increased attention to the long straight stretch of road ahead, changed gear noisily, and pulled over to the left to let a non-existent car pass. My studious checking of the left-hand mirror, the rear mirror, the right-hand mirror, and the three mirrors a second needless time, was the nearest I came to shaking my head in negation.

"There you are", exclaimed Kit triumphantly. "You b'lieve Bryn, doncha?"

"I believe Bryn, but I 'erd **you** say me name. Now, what I wanna know is what was you sayin' about me?"

"We wasn't sayin' **nuff**ink about you"

"I 'erd you say 'Sonya'," thickly, angrily.

"Oh, yeah, now I know" said Kit with frenetic lightness of tone, and looking into my helpless eyes for inspiration. "Now I know", turning to the swiftly passing landscape outside the window. "**Now** I know what you mean". She turned and placed a comforting hand on Sonya's arm, and stared long and lovingly — and temporisingly — into her eyes. "What I said, Sonya (and I knew that the lightening of inspiration had earthed safely from the stormy skies) "What I said was not 'Sonya'. Not **'Sonya'**. What I said was 'Sod yuh'." You see, Bryn is always trying to persuade me to come to class, ain't you, Bryn?"

I felt that I could readily assent to this query without reference to the driving mirrors, and did so.

"An' I get sick of it, man. So when he started again this afternoon, I told 'im straight, "Sod yuh, Bryn, I said, I'm not bee coming to class". Her voice rose in familiar stridence, mounting the stirrup of a well-worn hobby-horse.

Through the driving mirror I could see that Sonya's attention was shared with the beginning of the narration of a joke behind.

"It's my life, ain't it? I've a right to learn or not, so I said, 'Sod yuh Bryn'. Don't you agree, Sonya? Don't you think I have the right to decide to go to class or not?"

Sonya shrieked and rolled about as the joke reached its creaking conclusion. Kit, with a broad grin and a wink to me which belied the intensity of her discourse, continued to berate the iniquities of our class system.

Protecting One's Image

Following a telephone call from her Social Worker, I had invited Kit to a private room to impart some news to her.

We sat reminiscing about her two years' sojourn at the school, which was in effect its history, since she was its fifth pupil in its second week.

"Do you remember when you came to meet me on Derby Bus Station. An' I was stood there with ol' Mrs. Kirkham, me Social Worker, holdin' me Teddy in me arms . . ."

"Hiding **behind** him, you mean. It was a **huge** Teddy. Mrs. Kirkham carried your luggage, 'coz your arms were full . . ."

"An' you come up to see me, an' said, 'Ello Christine. Welcome to your new school' an' I said, "Piss off, you wanker. Me name's not Chris**tine**, an' I'm not coming to your rotten school".

"And poor Mrs. Kirkham. She must have felt that if you had come for interview, then you'd failed it. So you would've if we hadn't needed the fees for you".

"Yeh: she was a real tow-rag, w'nt she? I **'ated** 'er, with 'er 'Christine this' an' 'Christine that' . . . La-di-dah".

"No, she wasn't. If anyone was a foul-mouthed tow-rag on that day it was you. She was, as I remember her, a pleasant, educated, middle-class lady, who was trying to do her best for an ill-tempered, ungrateful brat. It isn't her fault she was middle-class".

"Yes, but Bryn, she wuz me third social worker in the two years since me Mum died. Right cows, all of 'em".

"Well, you've got to remember that at the age of fourteen you were a very disturbed child, and you'd have hated **any**one at that time".

"Yeh. Do you remember 'ow you used to send me to me room and 'ow

I used to swear and bang me foot on **ev**ery stair as I wen' up. I **was** a little sod".

"The swearing I didn't mind so much: it was that horripilating cry from your heart that got through to me".

"You mean 'I don't care. I don't CARE'?" "I DON'T CA-A-ER".

"You don't need to remind me of it, thanks, Kit. It's graven on my memory. The cry of a soul who wished she didn't exist — violently. Personal abuse is nothing compared to that desperate shriek of yours".

"That was what I was shoutin' when you took me Teddy off me that time, w'nt it?"

"Yes, and I don't need reminding of that **either**, thank you. One of the most despicable acts of my professional life. Poor little girl. Child-handled to her room, so she screams 'I don't care' and seizes the only article of comfort in her life, her Teddy. So the big strong headmaster wrenches it off her and flings it out of the bedroom".

"Yes, it **was** a rotten thing to do, but you got to admit that I did stop shouting, an' we 'ad our first **real** talk together that afternoon".

"True. Your shouting changed to pitiful sobbing. When I come to write my memoirs I will explain what a carefully thought-out strategy on my part it was, but you and I will know that it was the act of a desperate man with that frightful shrilling in my ears. The funny thing is that my whole life seems a series of mistaken moves which have led to the solution of the particular problem which beset me at the time. And you certainly were a major problem in my life at the time".

"Sure thing. But ne' mind. I do care **now**. Since I got **my** problem wi' me ole man sorted out, an' I found meself a new mum 'n dad".

"Yes, with dear old Sylvia and Roger in your life now as your Befrienders, you hardly need a social worker any more, do you?" (I was now steering the conversation round to the piece of news I had to impart).

"Now 'sfunny you should say that, Bryn. I bin thinkin' a lot about Greg recently. Not **only** 'cause he's a hunky young man — 'fore **you** say it — but he's bin a real fren' to me, not like all them other Social Workers I 'ad. They were **filth**. Five in four years. Huh! An' I gave Greg some stick w'en 'e wuz 'al-lo-cated to my case'. Do you 'member? I wun't speak to 'im w'en we wuz introduced. Jus' stood there wi' me arms folded, wi' me 'ed on one side, with **that** smile on me face that I know gets people's goat. An' 'e jus' talked to me gentle, an' said as 'ow 'e wuz sorry 'e 'ad caught me at a bad moment, an' if it wuz inconvenient 'e would come an' see me again. All the way from London! W'en 'e left I felt **awful**. Do you 'member?"

"Yes, he's a real gentleman, is Greg. But I would put in a word for the four other poor devils who were unfortunate enough to be 'al-lo-cated to your case'. I am not speaking out of professional loyalty, or any of that . . . crap. I am trying to address myself to your state of mind. It's bad **for your sake** to harbour hateful feelings, even towards people who are irrelevant to your life now. I ask you to seek to understand the social worker's situation when told to intervene in an already bad family relationship. In your case, the social worker had to remove you from your home because your father was ill-treating you . . ."

"On'y because 'e had a pig of an upbringin' 'isself. In that awful Kid's 'Ome, where 'e wuz beaten and starved as a punishment".

"Quite right, Kit. I'm not starting to knock your dad, not after all the conversations we have had about him, to seek to understand why he used to swear at you and knock you about, and why he favoured your brother".

"Not arf 'e did. After me mum died 'e used to belt me summink chronic. Wiv anyfink what come to 'and. Any ole bit of wood, or 'is bare fists. 'E di'nt **ca**-er. An' wunst 'e picked up a chair an' . . . "

The vividness of the memory overcame her, and she stopped mid-flight, her head suddenly dropping into the cup of her hand.

"I know, Kit. You've told me about that incident before. But if you have learnt to understand your father, who ill-treated you so grossly because of his upbringing, can you not try to understand all those social workers who didn't ill-treat you at all, but simply sought to act for your benefit. It was particularly unfortunate that the first one actually put **you** in a children's home which was so incompetently run that it had to close. But that wasn't the social worker's fault . . . altogether. She was seeking to remove you from a father who was a danger to you. I ask you to understand for **your** sake".

"See what y'mean", wiping her eyes with her sleeve.

"But, as I was saying earlier, you don't **need** a social worker any more now. You're a self-possessed young woman of 16, able to manage her own affairs . . ."

"Oh, yes I do. I still need to talk to Greg".

"You do? I thought . . . Well, I'd better come to the point. Greg phoned me this morning . . ."

"Oh, great! When's 'e comin' up?"

"Well, next week actually, but he phoned to tell me . . . to prepare you . . . so's it wouldn't come as too much of a . . . surprise . . ."

"What?

". . . that . . . that he's been offered promotion, and that he won't be able to . . . superintend you . . . your case any more . . . He sends you his best wishes and . . ."

"Oh, **naow**." Gone was the old brittle Cockney perkiness. For me her open-mouthed face has already been depicted in its hopeless vastation by Edvard Munch's painting, **Der Schrei**, but for Kit now it says, "I do care. I **do** care".

She rocks forward and her head falls into her hands. And her cup of misery runs over — through her fingers, down her wrists. I do not seek to staunch such a salutory grief, but pick up the telephone, fingers working urgently.

"Hello, Social Services Department, please . . ." I thought of this young man with another 30 or so years in his profession, "Greg Thomas, please".

Thirty thankless years of seeking to relate with the naked antagonism of hundreds of 14-year-old Kits. Let him have at least one moment of professional satisfaction.

"Hi, Greg. Bryn Here. Well, I've told Kit and . . . I'll pass the phone to her. Here you are, Kit".

"'Lo Greg. It in't true, is it?" A pause, and fresh gusts of unstaunchable sobbing at the reply.

I stand up, reach for the fag-scrip and the box of tissues, and lay them beside her before leaving the room.

On my return, ten minutes later, Kit sits red-eyed, with sodden paper tissues on the floor around her, but composed and pulling strongly on her cigarette.

"Thanks for the fag, Bryn. Ah well, what's gotta be, gotta be. Jus' one thing, though. You won't tell anyone 'bout me cryin' just because of me social worker's leavin', will y'?" She sniffed, and some of her old perkiness returned to her. "Bad for me image".

Trouble Up At T'Mill

At home, the phone rang. Eve's voice. A bad augur. It may mean that the staff are too preoccupied to come to the phone themselves.

"Neil says to tell you 'Red Light'". A catch in the voice. "You'd berrer 'urry, Bryn. Lyndy's flipped 'er lid again".

Too many times had I been called when the crisis was past its peak, and I had arrived to find only girls sitting with flushed cheeks and stertorous breathing. So I invited staff to call me on 'amber', or even 'green and amber', before the 'red light' flashed. They protested that they didn't wish to disturb my off-duty time at home, but I had insisted. The warning system had worked very well.

I had often dropped in 'unexpectedly' to find flashing eyes but no actual trouble, and thus had been able to intervene positively in crisis-prevention.

But this was the first 'Red'-call I had had after the introduction of our preventive policy. I reached 25 m.p.h. in second gear only to find a car cruising at 25 m.p.h. in the middle of the road, and oncoming traffic made overtaking dangerous . . .

Still three minutes wasn't bad from door to door under such circumstances, and I flexed my muscles, mentally and physically, as I entered the building at a fast lope.

Eve was waiting by the front door, knowing the importance of her post in this commissariat of information. She jerked a thumb. "Upstairs — Lyndy's bedroom". I used hands on both banisters to attain my five-stair stride. Her voice followed me up to the landing, "I've sent Alan up". Good old Eve. Alan was her 17 year-old boyfriend from the local estate, and, from the familiarity of his presence, the elder brother of the other girls. With the smoothness of transfer of Fred Trueman's run-up into his delivery stride, my fast lope up to Lindy's door had become a casual stroll as I entered her bedroom to find . . .

No one there . . . Anticlimax. I paused to locate where in the building the noise would be coming from . . . Silence throughout. Except . . . rapid phlegmmy breathing from the floor between the bunk-beds . . . and, as I became more aware of sound, the counterpoint of deeper, slower gaspings . . . from two sets of lungs.

I rounded the bed. Lyndy was face-down on the floor. Neil was sitting on the small of her back, grasping her wrists to the carpet. Alan was holding her ankles, and Carole was kneeling, gently stroking her tousled hair away from her face. My foot kicked into a broom-handle without a head, and it rolled noisily against the skirting. I picked it up as if tidying the room, chatted casually to Alan about his new job, and explained to Neil that I had come up to school to fetch a book for Meg, in order to give them time to ease their breathing . . .

I tidied the floor of the flotsam, or, rather, jetsam, of the conflict, and heard Neil's voice gently murmuring into Lyndy's ear. "Can we let you go now, duck?" . . . One wrist was freed. Then the other. Lyndy lay inert apart from the pumping of her lungs. "O.K. Alan, let her ankles go now. Thanks". Alan stood up, flexed his fingers, and smiled at me unsteadily. "Now, Lyndy, I couldn't let you keep that pole, could I? Especially when you were swinging it about your head and threatening Sheila with it . . . It's all right now . . . Have a good cry . . . if you can . . ."

I motion Alan to follow me out of the room, to leave Neil to his umpteenth counselling session this term with Lyndy.

We walk together down the stairs, to find Eve awaiting him. "Thanks Eve. Thanks Alan You deserve each other".

Quick stroll round the building ("What are you doing with that broom-handle, Bryn?") which is peaceful and friendly, as always after a discharge of emotion in the community.

I toss the casus belli in the back of the car, and drive home, having solved yet another spot of bother up at t'mill.

A Moment of Truth

I wanted to store something in the attic, up the telescopic ladder, which is housed in the ceiling space. I wandered about helplessly for a minute or two.

"Hey, Neil, where's the hooked pole to bring down the attic ladder?"

And slightly reprovingly, "I think we ought to keep it in its place, in case one of the girls uses it as a weapon when she's in a paddy".

Neil's eyes belied his serious expression. "As a matter of fact when **we** use it **we** always put it back in the right place behind your door. **We** realise that it's potentially dangerous".

He went off to look in the places where I had already been, and returned shortly, without the pole, but his eyes altogether more thoughtful.

"I can't find it, but I bet I know who's had it". He sat down. "Peter".

"Peter? Why would Peter need it? He's only just come on the staff and he doesn't know what's up in the attic".

"And I bet I know where it **is**".

"Besides, if he **had** borrowed it, he'd have put it back".

"And I'll show you where he put it". He stood up purposefully, and I trailed after him into Peter's room. "As you say, the pole is a weapon". He looked behind the wardrobe. "Of **def**ence as well as **off**ence". He pulled out the sofa. "Now where would Peter put it?"

"Peter? What would Peter want with a defensive weapon?"

"Where would Peter **put** a defensive weapon, more like . . . even when he sleeps . . ."

"But Peter's got a Black Belt".

"Ah!" He thrust his arm under the bed. "And **I've** got the pole".

"But my dear Watson" I exclaimed (for I'm not having anyone else playing Sherlock in **my** school), how did you deduce that the pole was under Peter's bed?"

"Elementary, Holmes", replied Neil, who often allows me to feel that I am in charge of affairs. "Did Jenny tell you about the incident in the kitchen the other evening?"

"No, what incident?"

"I told her to. How the hell does she, as a young member of staff, expect to learn, if she can't admit when things go wrong? I happened to walk into the kitchen on Tuesday after tea to find Jenny leaning backwards over the sink, with Lyndy holding an empty milk bottle in her face, threatening to smash it and cut her if she moved an inch. She looked evil, and she sounded evil, Bryn. She meant it. Well, she knew she wouldn't have to do it because she knew Jenny daren't move. But she meant to terrify her, and she was damn well succeeding. And she's so **clever**. She didn't choose a knife, which **is** an offensive weapon. She didn't break the bottle, so that there'd be a jagged edge. No, she was holding a bland, domestic milk bottle in her hand, and when I walked in her tone changed. I challenged her, and she said "We was only 'avin' a game, wasn't we, Jenny?"

"Jenny just smiled — she was still shaken — and agreed afterwards that she would see you about it. I should've told you myself".

"Well, you have now. I'll have a word with Jenny".

"I don't think that Jenny is the priority: it's Lyndy. There's something very threatening about her and she's very strong: she needs at least two people to hold her effectively. We need two males on duty. A person tackling her solo would be putting himself at risk.

And talking about males putting themselves at risk, perhaps we ought to consider seriously the risk to our masculinity in such a situation. You see, she never shows this side of herself to you".

"Perhaps we three ought to have a batsman's box as standard issue?"

"But the rest of us can suddenly be confronted with a wild little animal".

". . . and shin pads".

"Could you have a talk with her?"

"It's very courteous of you to suggest it, Neil, especially when you know that while she does what I bid her I haven't had a meaningful conversation with her since she came 6 months ago. If I try to talk with her human-to-human, she just grunts or keeps saying "pardon" so that the rhythm of ordinary conversation breaks down — like a front-wheel bicycle puncture; you're alright at the back: you keep pedaling like hell, but the bump-bump-bump makes you get off in the end. If I want to tell her anything, I always ask you to do it. You've invested hours in her. The assured, animated, smiling person I see with you is someone I've simply never met personally. You know that, so what good is it going to do? Do you mean that I ought to **tell** Lyndy something?"

"I'd rather not say. Let's see what Peter has to say when he comes on duty at 4 o'clock.

"Hi, Peter, did you find that little place near Hartington with the stream for your kids to play in and the hills all about? . . . Good, good. Delightful spot, isn't it! . . . I've got one or two more places round here to recommend you. But to business. We were looking for the loft-pole to-day".

"I'm terribly sorry. I'll go and . . ." heaving his considerable bulk out of his chair.

"No, no. Don't bother. Neil found it".

"Sorry for going into your room, Peter: I was just following a hunch".

"And Neil seems to know why you put it under your bed".

"For protection, quite simply, Bryn".

"Protection for your 15 stone, all muscle? Your Black Belt?"

"For myself, no. But I have a wife and two children in these rooms and the atmosphere in the evenings these last few days has been really ugly. Lyndy . . . "

"Ah, Lyndy . . . "

"Lyndy is so full of hate. She looks at you with those eyes . . . Well, you know what beautiful intelligent blue eyes she's got when she's laughing . . . when she used to laugh?"

"Dunno. Never seen her eyes. Always hanging her head when **I'm** about. And that damn' peaked cap she affects . . ." But Neil is nodding, listening intently.

"Well they change. As cold as ice, and yet as penetrating and destructive as a laser beam. And she's so physically strong for her size. I'm no chicken", extending open hams for our inspection; "but I'm aware that I have to exert myself when she play-fights with me, or rather she

pretends to play-fight with me. Because she means it. And her influence over the other girls . . . They're scared. And she gets them worked up to do what she wants. Which brings me back to the pole. There was a potential riot last night at 11.30. I nearly phoned you for help, Bryn — for the first time in nearly 10 years working with disturbed kids".

"I didn't realise it had got so bad".

"I was going to talk to you about it this afternoon. She's so clever. She's always joking — with an edge to it. So you smile, and try to take it in good part. Then she cuts again, even closer to the bone. The other girls cackle. You challenge. Then it's 'Only a joke'. So she's got a reason to turn nasty. 'Can't you take a joke?' Then tea ends in miserable silence, Lyndy all injured innocence. We sit there spoilsports, chewing away at our food, giving ourselves ulcers in 5 years time".

"Phew! As bad as that".

"No, worse, because there are another four hours before bedtime".

"So, what are we going to do about it?" said the Headmaster.

"I don't think we have an alternative. I think she has to go".

"Expelled? But we can't lose her fee" rejoined the Bursar, "I've just ordered carpets for the bedrooms".

"I agree with Peter", said Neil. "I know money's important, Bryn, but we've got to consider whether you want to lose the whole community. We've lost the community spirit already".

"But you've always been so close to Lyndy".

"I still am, and I still like her a lot. That is, I still like the person that I have private conversations with. But she's poisoning the community, and I think that with three new staff and two new girls we've got to balance priorities and admit we can't handle this problem".

". . . Right, I'll phone the Authority right away, and tell them that, regretfully, we'll have to send her home to-morrow morning. I don't like doing it. The only other time I actually expelled anyone, I gave the Authority two month's notice. Anyway, there's one person who'll be delighted by the news: Lyndy. She's always hated the place since she arrived 6 months ago.

Lyndy was chattering and smiling happily as she entered the Common-room with Neil at his invitaion, but ceased abruptly as soon as she registered my presence. My own cordial smile and air of welcome were lost on her, as her head was once again hanging, further obscured by that wide-peaked cap.

"Hi, Lyndy. Come and sit down, won't you?" Loud, avuncular, false-sounding.

"?" she grunted.

"I said, Hi, Lyndy, come and sit down, won't you?" Bump, bump, bump.

"?" again. The peaked cap peered about the room as if chairs had not been invented.

"Over here, next to me", I answered, patting the chair-arm reassuringly.

She stilted woodenly over to a chair across the room, near to Neil, and collapsed into it, like a rag doll thrown by a petulant child. The musculature was nerveless; only the peaked cap remained alert, with the bristling alertness of a hand-held shield ready for the conflict.

Neil moved his chair, in a pre-arranged strategic move, both to inhibit an eruption into the community and to bring himself closer to Lyndy for reassurance.

"I've got some good news for you, Lyndy". The shield tensed. "I'm painfully aware that you have not been happy at the school". No limb or digit moved, but I was aware that the whole musculature was now rigid where it had been nerveless a few moments before. To my practised eye it was the tenseness of preparation for sudden movement, for a bolt through the door. I glanced at Neil to confirm that he had picked up the signals and was himself alert, and came to the point quickly, in order to set her mind at rest. "So I've decided to allow you to go home, Lyndy".

There was a long pause. This time Neil did not need to interpret for me, as the peaked-cap jerked up and she looked first at Neil and then at me. Golly, Peter was right; she had beautiful eyes, intelligent and feeling. Feeling eyes, hurt eyes, angry eyes.

"You allow me, but I ain't goin'. I do what *I* want to do; I go where *I* want to go, not where you **allow** me to go". Not quite the response we had expected, but a decision is a decision. My voice dropped its avuncularity and honed to a cutting edge.

"I respect your firmness in determining your life, Lyndy, but you must allow me to determine the kind of school we wish to run. I will not permit bullying of staff or pupils. I will not permit snide 'jokes' which hurt. We do not want a school in which we have the kind of physical conflict you have been engaged in with the staff recently".

The trajectory of her eyes met mine, and was steady. Something unseen in their depths encouraged a softening of my tone.

"But above all, Lyndy, we don't want girls here who are not happy. What's the point? I could expel you for some misbehaviour, but you might find it difficult to find another school, with an expulsion in your record. So I'm allowing you to choose to go home — but . . . it must be clearly understood, I am not allowing you to choose to stay at this school".

A long silence of fixed staring, to measure me for perhaps the first time, followed by the sudden closing of the louvre.

Neil began to interpret as usual. "Bryn means what he says. He seems pretty easy-going, but when he makes a decision like this he sticks to it".

Her two eyes turned on mine again. Deep eyes, liquid with unshed tears, in which I saw scenes where her father habitually hit her, sometimes with a clenched fist, once against a wall . . . where her brother may have . . . where teachers snapped at her in class for her restlessness, where her mother threatened to send her away from home . . . And now she was being rejected back home. Her eyes dropped, and a rivulet coursed unheeded down her cheeks, off her chin and a stain began to spread on

73

her jacket.

Her voice, when she began to speak, was tired, weary with sadness. "I just like to say that I'm sorry for 'ow I bin lately, that I'm very sorry. I just like to say that I *do* like the school an' I *do* like the staff and I don't know what's made me act so rotten to you all, but . . . I'm sorry".

Over the years my mind has aimed at an aurelian impassivity to the unexpected, and to some extent has acquired it; but Lyndy's words were, and remain, the biggest surprise of my professional life.

Her eyes continued to hold mine, still coursing tears. (My mind recalled my only bull-fight. A young toro was in its death-throes in the arena in Alicante years before. It had begun strong and hungry for the kill, cavorting and charging the bandilleros one after the other till they ran for the exit. But now it stood amidst the plashes of its own gore, brave head hung, staring at the matador advancing stilly and intently, blade poised).

Our eyes remained focussed on each other. At one level my mind continued to recreate imaginatively what people had inflicted on Lyndy to make her into the person she had become; at another, it recalled reasons why a resolute decision had to be taken to rid the community of the threat to its stability. The moment of truth.

My voice had its decisive cutting edge as I began my response. "Yes, Lyndy, but you have caused a deep disturbance in the school, and, as I say, we don't want you to be here if you're not happy". My eyes dropped from hers, and there followed a long pause. "But are you saying that you would like to stay?"

Eyes glistening under the louvre. "Yes".

"Do you think you can be happy here?"

Glistening and brightening, "Yes".

"And will you apologise to Jenny, as you have just done to us, for threatening her with a milk bottle the other evening? . . . No, no, I didn't mean immediately, m' dear. Stay here and talk to Neil while I go and get you both a cup of coffee . . ."

To Mansfield

Well, you've got to admit that Jane *had* had a very troubled three weeks, but that cannot wholly excuse her rudeness to the headmaster.

She had been admitted to school on Monday and had absconded twice in four days, once overnight. She had smashed a window, been taken to hospital, and picked random and motiveless quarrels with a positively mackenroe ferocity and perseverance of expression.

And it didn't help not to know which home she was going each weekend. Was it to the Children's Home, to this foster parent or that? She had slept in three officially-designated beds in two weekends, quite apart from absconding and sleeping elsewhere from Sunday to Wednesday this week. The reason she has stayed with us for 48 hours is because we took her high-heeled shoes away.

It is Friday morning.

"Which 'ome am I going to today, Bryn?"

"I thought your social worker phoned you last night and told you that you are going to foster-parents at Mancester.

"I ain't goin' to bleedin' Manchester".

"No, no. Man**ces**ter. Your new foster parents in Mancester".

"Me noo foster parents are in **Mansfield**. And what about me case and things that I left at me **old** foster parents when I done a bunk on Sunday?"

"Well, let's deal with one thing at a time" (I am aware that Clare, another new girl at the end of her first week overhears our conversation and I wish to give an impression of clear-sighted organising power and incisiveness). "I telephoned your social worker last night and I talked with the taxi-firm this morning. There is no question about where you are going. You are going to Mancester".

"No I'm pissin' not. I'm goin' to bleedin' Mansfield. I know the pissin' road, I know the bleedin' number".

"Yes, that's the address, but the house is in Mancester, a hundred miles away".

"Mansfield . . .

. . . "Mancester . . .

. . . bleedin' . . . pissin' . . .

My incisiveness in shreds, I remark on the painting which Clare is engaged on.

It is Friday afternoon. The taxi has arrived. Jane asks for her shoes. The member of staff who has sequestrated them is off duty and out of the building . . . I feverishly search the drawers. I engage Neil's help and we go into all the staff rooms. Jane is panicking about going home and **she** doesn't even **know** we can't find her only pair of shoes. Meg comes along and finds them in one of the drawers I had looked in a few minutes before. She leaves them at the top of the stairs and goes off to get Jane ready for the taxi. I pick up the shoes and go out to explain the delay to the taxi-driver. Nice breath of fresh air. Calming.

. . . "Oh, and don't tell her she's going to Mancester".

"But they've told me at the Education that she **is** going to Mancester".

"Yes, but . . .

"Oh, I thought . . .

"Yes, Mansfield **is** in Nottinghamshire, but . . .

"Oh, . . . "

I return inside the building to find an even tenser atmosphere than before. Meg greets me grave-faced.

"Jane is rampaging round the school now. Can you hear her upstairs? She asked for her shoes, and I told her that they were at the top of the stairs. She says she can't find them, and I **know** I put them there, so either someone's taken them spitefully to upset her, or she's hidden them herself to get a bit of attention . . . But . . . " as we hear shrillness and the sound of stockinged boots upstairs, "she does sound **gen**uinely upset" . . .

Margaret didn't seem as grateful as I thought she might have been when I solved the problem by producing the shoes from where I had been casually holding them behind my back . . . but at least Jane is happy.

She came to say goodbye to Meg and to have one last passage-at-arms with me.

"Well, where they tekkin' me this weekend, Bryn?"

I answered clearly and incisively, "To Mansfield".

She sniffed disappointedly, and turned on clacking heels to the door. "Got a bit of pissin' sense at last, I'm glad to see".

The Curious Incident of the Dog in the Night

As we entered the front door, Neil and Tim stood grinning gleefully in welcome.

"You're for it. Jane's gunning for you". She hasn't stopped talking since half past eight".

"What have **I** done?"

Tim shook his locks, cheerfully determined not to be reassuring "I don't think there's any chance of your arguing your way out of what you've **done**; it's what you **are** that you will be required to defend".

I assume a tense, bent-kneed attitude of defence before the dining-room door, behind which Jane's raised voice even now is heard, and then dart forward, kick the door open and, lacking a stetson, throw in my brief case as a decoy. I then advance into the room, six-guns blazing . . .

Maureen, the Play Group Supervisor, smiles her good morning. I suppose she's getting used to me. However, Jane is suitably impressed, and I achieve my aim by rendering her unaccustomedly speechless, mid-harangue.

I pick up my brief case, dust it with two expertly casual brushes on the chaps of my trousers, and roll out through the swing-doors up to the Common Room.

A minute or two later Neil opens the door of the Common Room.

"There's a young lady downstairs from the Y.T.S. or something, whom **we** weren't expecting, but who says **you** are".

"Oh, yes, it's Fiona from a local secondary school. Come in, Fiona. You're coming on a day's visit to-day aren't you, before your full week next week. Well, you're very welcome, even though no one but me knows who you are and why you've come. You see, it's a little initiative test I like to set the staff and visitors to the school. I like to keep the staff on their toes by not telling them what's happening from hour to hour, and I begin to train visitors to be prepared for the unexpected from the moment they stand on the threshold and begin to wonder, from the blank looks, if they've come to the right place at all. Now, have you met everyone?"

"Well, not really. As soon as I went in the dining-room, Jane started to talk to me, and has been ever since, till now, when Neil brought me here".

"Oh", with real concern, "Jane's **not** an initiative test I had planned or would have subjected you to".

"It's all right" Fiona smiles easily. "She seems upset about something. She's lost her trainers, she says, and all sorts of things have gone wrong for her recently".

I conclude that this assured and friendly young woman has passed her initiative test, and we prepare for the Moot.

Opening the Moot, I declare my intention of explaining the whole purpose of the school, to new girls and visitor.

"Our aim is to facilitate, that means make easy, or help, children grow up, to become adults. Every person of whatever age is adult in some areas and infantile in others. Infantile means 'childish', but I prefer not to use that word, as it can be a term of abuse. We are all adult sometimes, we are all infantile sometimes. I include myself . . ."

"Especially you", interjects Jane. "You'd forget your bleedin' 'ead if it wasn't screwed on". She had been standing looking out of the window since we had gathered, but now turns and projects herself, voice and gesture, at me.

"As Jane is kind enough to remind us, I have my faults like anyone else . . ."

"Bleedin true you 'ave. Nut case if you ask me".

I reach for my six-guns at my belt, but find only comfortable middle-age spread. Why couldn't the blessed girl fire off her salvoes and then make a noisy and dramatic exit, like all the others who had suddenly — but briefly — shattered the peace of the Moot over the years. But Jane stands there, arms akimbo, slightly swaying, with a fixed grin of defiance and calculated insolence. I catch Fiona's look of frozen horror. So this is what a Special School is like, it says. However, Jane has achieved her aim by rendering me unaccustomedly speechless. I may have no recourse to six-guns, but at least I can climb on to my high-horse.

"If you are not able to address the Moot in a proper manner . . ."

"I don't care a sod for the Moot"

" . . . then you ought to leave it . . ."

"Not till I've got me bleedin' rights".

" . . . and if you don't . . ."

"Yeh, an' if I don't?"

" . . . then we shall have to take you out".

"Oh yeh? You and whose bleedin army?"

Me and my bleedin' army, I think. "Will you help me, please, Tim and Neil?"

I was half way up from my chair when, happily, Jane changes tack.

"You aint layin' a finger on me", and, with a skirr of feet on the carpet, the electric flash of blue dressing-gown, and the thunder of slammed door, she is gone.

I resume my accustomed speechfulness

" . . . As I was saying, we are each of us adult at times and infantile at others. Our aim is to work together, child and adult of whatever age, to help each other, to become more sensitive to each others' feelings, to become more responsible for each others' behaviour. We must not split into groups, and become antagonistic one group to another. We have had incidents when girls of different coloured skin have become hostile to each other. It's difficult to believe, isn't it, with black girls and white girls sitting here today in friendship and wondering what nonsense I'm talking now. But it has happened, about 18 months ago that the white girls were sitting on one side of this room in a specially-convened Moot, and the black girls on the other. There were a nasty few minutes, while I talked about how irrational it was, and then girls from both sides joined in the conversation to agree that we wanted a happy community, that is to say a collection of people who live together, eat together, laugh together and weep together, without division of skin-colour. I can refer to that time, because some of you will remember it, and the others will think it's a trivial issue to get worked up about.

"But at the moment I believe that people are creating splits in the community, not on the basis of colour, but of age. Instead of working together, some girls are thinking about divisions of age, of the girls being somehow significantly different from the adults. They are 'ageist' not 'racist'. For instance, the other day, when the dinner tables were set together, some girls consciously separated them and sat on one table, leaving the Staff to sit on another. I appeal to them not to deny themselves the maturing process and to join the adult race . . . "

"That's all very well" says Clare, two-weeks new at the school, highly intelligent, with the adolescent's healthy desire to reform the world before dusk, "but why didn't you invite Jane to join the adult race, as you call it? Why didn't you let her speak?"

"I hear you, Clare. You are being sensitive to Jane's needs, and responsible in helping her to voice them. I'm afraid that she is so antagonistic to the adult world that she can't bring herself to speak to me civilly. Do you think that you could invite her to return to put her case reasonably and articulately?"

"Yes, I think I could". And with an impatient flounce she is gone, to return a minute later with Jane in tow. (It will be tricky enough to juggle with Jane's open-wound susceptibilities without having the additional ball of Clare's hostility-to-adults in the air. But Jane starts well.)

"I'd just like to say sorry for shouting the first time, but I was very annoyed about me trainers. Somebody's pinched me trainers. I don't want to mention no names, but only two people know I've got any trainers at school. So they must've pinched 'em, an' if they don't bring 'em back by 8 o'clock tonight, there's going to be trouble . . . "

Chairgirl: "Tracey".

"What you tryin' to say then? Are you tryin' to say as me an' Barbara took your trainers".

"I ain't sayin' no names. I'm on'y sayin' as on'y two people in this school know I 'ad me trainers in me 'oldall, and now I'm sayin' they bin pinched".

"An' I'm on'y sayin' that as me an' Barbara was in your room it must be us you're talkin' about". Tracey leans forward, finger pointed tremblingly . . .

"Point of order, Chairgirl. I've had my hand up ever since Jane first used the word 'pinched', and before either Tracey put hers up or Jane spoke out of order".

Chairgirl: "Oh, alright then, Bryn".

"Firstly, I'd like to thank Clare for bringing Jane back in the Moot. Secondly, I appreciate that Jane was able to speak for the first time in a Moot. Where do you think she got the idea of 'mentioning no names'? It is one of our Moot-practices, but she got that idea out of her own head. The trouble is that we all know who she's talking about, as she told everyone which two girls she suspected earlier this morning. I understand Tracey's sense of grievance . . . "

"You understand Tracey's grievance all right, but what are you doing about poor Jane's trainers that've been pinched?" Clare's throbbing concern threatens the balls already in the air. Jane, encouraged by the mounting tension of the court-room drama, shrills accusingly, "Yeah, what are you doin' about me trainers?"

"What we are doing about the trainers is that all of us are sitting here trying to talk about them in a rational way to discover where they may be. If Clare will help Jane talk calmly, and if Tracey would tell us whatever she knows about the missing trainers, as responsibly and honestly as we know she usually does, then I feel sure that Jane will have satisfaction from the processes of the Moot".

Tim: "Perhaps it might be said that if Tracey **has** the trainers, it would have been very responsible to take them, since Jane isn't allowed footwear of any sort in case she absconds".

Tracey: "No, I ain't took 'em", and thus endorses her innocence by her response to Tim's shrewd Winslow-boy strategem.

Jane (uninvited by the Chairgirl): "Well, how did they get out of my suitcase when you were in my room last night?"

Tracey bridles, but with many moot-hours experience behind her, looks at me, and, drawing assurance from my long slow nod, replies with

79

dignity, "I only said that I didn't take your trainers. In fact, I didn't even **see** your trainers. I was in your room, like you say, but . . .

Jane (again uninvited): "So, you're saying I'm a liar".

Bryn (uninvited) "Point of order. No, Jane. She did **not** say that. You must listen to what she **did** say. She has spoken with great restraint".

Jane (uninvited): "So **you** think I'm a liar do you? You're taking 'er side, are you?"

Bryn: "In response to your question, the purpose of the Moot is to register what we perceive to have happened, that is to say, 'The truth', and we have spent the last 10 minutes seeking the truth for your benefit, and . . ." The door slammed once more behind Jane's outraged back, so I perorate rather lamely, "and we all want to be on your side". I draw breath and, entering and lengthening my therapeutic stride, change tack.

"We all want to be on Jane's side because we realise that her emotions have been deeply damaged at some time during her childhood. Regarding how she behaves now, I conjecture that she has undergone great suffering, probably cruelty, at the hands of an adult who knew no better and who had a deprived childhood; I conjecture that, as the years passed, her behaviour has become more and more strange and even wild, as we witness it now, until other children begin to call her 'loopy', 'mental' or 'mad'. I know that some of you here now have been subjected to similar unkindness and will empathise with Jane. And there will have been certain children, themselves emotionally disturbed, who realised that a lot of malicious fun could be made out of Jane, and who themselves worked on her weakness until she lost control of herself and began to behave erratically. Great fun for the bystanders! Like the television. Press the knob. Spin the dial, and sit back and enjoy yourselves! Look at poor Jane making a fool of herself once more! May I take this opportunity to explain to you all and to reassure some of you, that you do not come to this school if you are mentally ill. If you are mentally ill, then a psychiatrist will send you to a hospital; it is only if you are emotionally disturbed that a psychologist will decide that you come to a special school, that is, a school that specialises in restoring damaged emotions. Now I do understand why some of you thought, — and covertly said — a fortnight ago when Jane arrived that she was mad, because she **acted** like a mad person. And I will concede that if you subject a person long enough, and severely enough, to emotional stress, then it may affect the balance of his mind, just as if you continue to poison the lungs with nicotine it will eventually affect the heart. But", I pause long and look at each girl in the Moot before continuing "I can assure you that Jane is a perfectly normal person, with a good brain, a friendly personality, and **basically** healthy emotions. And, don't take my word for it. I'm not a psychiatrist, a mind-doctor, so I don't offer opinions about psychiatric matters. I don't even ask you to take my word for it because I've been observing Janes, and Traceys and Clares healing themselves and growing up for nearly 20 years. I ask you to review what you have witnessed this morning. I ask you to recall the Jane who was rampaging around the school an hour ago, accusing people left, right and centre of stealing her trainers, and threatening what she'd do to them. But people reacted calmly to her and simply advised her to raise her grievance in the Moot.

"I ask you to recall the Jane who stood in this Moot half-an-hour ago. It was her first Moot, and she didn't know how to conduct herself, and I know that she abused and threatened me . . . but she did come to present her case as she had been advised. Then she withdrew herself. With dignity, if not with grace. I have known many less troubled withdrawals from this Moot over the years" (Stella acknowledges my glance with a wry smile, so I continue) "I've known very assured young women collapse under the pressure of the Moot and blackguard me and bellow at everyone down each step of the stairs. But not Jane. One bang, and she was gone.

"I ask you to recall the Jane who returned to sit — not stand — in the Moot a quarter of an hour ago. Did she not apologise to me for her earlier rudeness? Did she not **begin** to put her grievance well? Are those the signs of the mentally ill person? Could a mentally ill person learn so much in an hour? I offer you my lay opinion that Jane matured about 5 years in 60 minutes — thanks to Tracey and Barbara, who endured what I consider her false accusations without retaliation; thanks to Fiona, who walked into our community this morning and sat down and listened patiently to Janet's outpourings to take the heat out of her; thanks to Clare for befriending her and inviting her back to the Moot. I very much appreciate the adult and responsible way in which those girls responded to Jane's infantile cries for help this morning. Which brings me back to what I began to say at the beginning of this Moot about my aim for this community to become one of caring and responsible adults . . . But I see a gleam in Clare's eye . . . If I don't return to the subject of the missing trainers, she will think I'm all tongue and no teeth.

"I am going to broach this problem as rationally and dispassionately as I may. There are three obvious hypotheses: 1) that Jane has lost or misplaced her trainers and, in good faith, doesn't remember where she put them; 2) that someone, unknown as yet, stole them, either for gain or maliciously; and 3) that Jane may have hidden her own trainers".

Fiona looks her incomprehension at the third hypothesis.

"You see, when a child has been so massively deprived of human love and the common care to which we all have a right in infancy, he or she devises means of attracting that attention. He becomes naughty, and his mother clouts him. Not quite what he wanted, so he tries being 'good' — mother ignores him, so he mithers her again. Another clout, harder this time. Not at all what he wanted, but it's better than being ignored. In a very profound way, he needs to feel that he 'exists' before he feels 'approved-because-he's-good'. And so it is with our Jane. She is drawing our attention to her the whole time, by absconding, by breaking a window, by swearing, and now, if the hypothesis is correct, she has found the most subtle means so far. She may or may not know whether she has 'lost' her trainers; her innermost self knows she needs care and attention. I suspend judgement over her trainers; which is, if you'll forgive me, Clare, relatively unimportant; I believe her totally when she 'tells' us that she needs our loving care". Fiona smiles her comprehension, and encouragement. And, in my storytelling I need little encouragement.

"Curiously enough, Janet reminds me very vividly of a girl who was here 3 or 4 years ago. She came from a Children's Home, as Jane does, she disliked me intensely, as Jane does, and she . . . well, let me tell you a little story, which I call **The Case of the Phantom Snatcher.**

". . . and that was the case of a girl who knew her needs and adopted devious means to meet them".

Tracey: "I think Bryn's right. I don't believe she ever 'ad a pair of trainers. Leastways, we never saw none when we was in there last night, did we, Barbara?"

Bryn: (with finger upraised in support of schoolmasterly punctilio) "I did not claim that I was right, Tracey. I merely expounded an hypothesis".

Carol: "Well, can't we leave your hypothesis or whatever you call them and get on and try and find the trainers?"

Further discussion took place, leading to a general search for the missing trainers when the Moot dispersed.

It was Playgroup morning, and the mothers were coming to collect their children. One, whom I knew slightly, drew close to where I was standing, being avuncular to the little ones.

"Excuse me" she said.

"Of course, Norma".

"Did you find the Yorkshire Terrier?"

I filled my lungs with air to answer what was evidently meant to be a civil question, and then expelled it again, as I tried to recall the Yorkshire Terriers of my acquaintance.

"The Yorkshire Terrier?"

"Yes"

"I think it got run over".

"Oh, I *am* sorry". The pathos in the voice did not communicate itself to her eyes, which became hard, as they sought to probe my unconcern. I am a dog-lover and wish to dispel the hardness in her gaze.

"Yes, it was always running into the street. Not surprisingly really".

"No, I suppose not" . Why was her stare so unyielding?

"Must have been six months ago"

"Six months?"

"Or nine".

"No, no. I'm talking about the Yorkshire Terrier you lost on Tuesday".

"Tuesday? But — I haven't got a Yorkshire Terrier. I thought you meant . . .

"Well not you personally. I mean one of your girls".

82

"One of the girls?"

"Yes, on Tuesday night this girl come into the chip shop where I was serving. There was quite a queue. She burst in, crying her eyes out. She was so obviously upset that I had to stop serving. A lady in the queue put her arm round her and asked her what was the matter".

"I've lost me Yorkshire Terrier", she said.

"Where did you see it last, me duck?"

"Down t'road"

"You'll have to go t'police station, luv".

"I've bin t'police station. They won't help me. I bet if it was an Alsation they'd try and find it. But it's only a little Yorkshire terrier . . . "

At this piece of unreason the dawn of comprehension begins to break in my mind.

" . . . so I asked her for her address so that we could contact her in case we found the dog, and she said that she lives at your school. I wondered why she was out that late at night".

Of course, of course, Norma. I didn't know you meant **that** Yorkshire Terrier. Would you mind waiting for a moment . . . ? I'll be back. I'll be back". And I leave poor Norma with her mouth open in dismay, having had her second distressing and mystifying encounters in 3 days . . .

"Clare, Fiona. Come quickly. I want you to meet a friend of mine called Norma . . .

" . . . Thank you for waiting for me, Norma, and I'd like you to tell Carol and Fiona here the curious incident of the dog last night . . . ".

Contradictions: Responsibilitarianism and Preventitivism

If you have borne with me so far, and have enjoyed the action, you may find this chapter a touch schoolmasterly. So I issue a Reader's Hazard warning that the unwary may be subject to an effusion of what dear old Mr. Polly called 'sesquipeldan verbojoose'. I mean to say, look at the title. It is a scratching of several of my professional itchings.

So feel welcome to close your books now and go out to play. After break-time I shall have a cracker of a story for you: an absconding, a Police chase, an attempted suicide — and the dénouement! When life has such turns of event, what need of fiction?

Responsibilitarianism

Those who remain may well ask themselves how anyone can enjoy caring for disturbed, angry, foul-mouthed, quarrelsome, young women going through the already prickly stage of adolescence, and behaving as infants, with none of infancy's charming redeeming features. A simple answer is that for much of the time I don't. Who would? So what is the reason for continuing in such a specialism? The French have a mot for it: Les fous cherchent le bonheur: les sages choisissent leur malheur.

I began my teaching career with a belief in freedom, in libertarianism. Within the teaching profession, the area in which one has the highest degree of freedom is with the unschoolable. The authorities, the Educational Authorities, are happy to give one a free hand with the children who have made life intolerable for, successively, the classteacher, the headteacher, the board of school governors, the Educational Authority. I suppose that it might be called, **pace** Ivan Illich, a rather unconvivial form of de-schooling.

All very well: one has enough freedom. The trouble is that one's charges have had too much, have run wild, have drunk **too** deep of the Libertarian spring.

The antidotes to such intoxication are increasing doses of control: mild discouragement, positive dissuasion, restraint, rigorous physical containment. The unhappy libertarian finds himself exercising an authoritarian strategy, totally antithetical to the philosophy with which he first became affianced. Serve him right for marrying for love in the first place, perhaps. But libertarian or authority-figure, must man be one?

Is there not a middle-ground, avoiding the excesses of both libertarianism and authoritarianism? Since I know no word to describe this neutral, but positive, ground of reconciliation, I am become neologist, and present the world with 'responsibilitarianism'. The responsibilitarian, in the specialist field of behaviour-control of which I write, may react to, or, literally, 'is able to respond to', situations according to contingency. **This** child may need any of various degrees of firmness or restraint: **that** one any of the various degrees of latitude or trust. Thus responsibilitarianism permits me to remain enamoured of my first-love, 'freedom', and take 'authority' to wife.

Preventivism

Very well, the curious enquirer may probe; you find that your chosen middle-ground was not a high-point after all, and you are playing your professional game of life with alligators on a low-lying swamp. What about draining the swamp? Do you **have** to deal with disturbed children as late as their mid-teens? Surely the behaviours which you describe in these pages could have been spotted earlier. Quite apart from other considerations, such as, for instance, the cost involved in such highly specialised educational provision, why in the name of humanity were those children, now young women, allowed to suffer both so acutely and so chronically?

My answer to such a question reveals another contradiction. I am both a care taker of disturbed young people on the verge of leaving school **and** a devout votary of Preventivism.

A devout and **practising** votary of Preventivism. Early in our career Meg and I ran a day school for disturbed children. We entered into a close rapport with local headteachers, particularly of Infant Schools, and so sensitive did they and their class-teachers become that our proportional intake of 5 to 7 year olds was well over 50% during the period when the national average for the admission of maladjusted infant-school-age children was point nought something. And what a turnover! It would have made any Director of Education or Keeper of the Municipal purse-strings pink with pleasure at its very cost-effectiveness, never mind the number of children whose stresses were relieved at such an early age.

At about this time, during the early seventies, our school was served by a dynamic young educational psychologist, who sought to promote the principle of preventive referral. He was very green then, of course. First post. Keen as mustard. But didn't know the ropes. One of his first tasks was to diagnose and refer a 9-year-old girl. Long years of tension between the parents before they had shattered apart. And the children, the shards of their family, lay about in various forms of emotional jaggedness. Carla was the most obviously and most urgently in need. Been stealing for years, till it had become compulsive with her. Her teachers and headteacher had been putting in ever more urgent termly requests for psychological action. Open and shut case, you see. An experienced and perceptive educational psychologist would have sorted the case out in a mere 6 months. A particularly astute child psychiatrist might have had the whole matter wrapped up, signed, sealed and delivered, in a single year. But my new friend, still wet behind the ears, took a mortal, livelong, ten whole days to transfer Carla from her primary to our special school. He received a strong letter of reprimand from the authorities — a month or two later, when they realised what had happened.

Undismayed, he and I planned the takeover and transformation of a small area of England — we talked about Rutland — to act as a model of how a sensitive referral system ought to be run. The authorities must have heard of our planned **coup d'éducation**, because they concocted some rather elaborate plot to foil our intentions, and, to our dismay, we found that Rutland had been annihilated, my friend removed out of good's way, to become Chief Psychologist of a large borough, and myself appointed to caretake a much larger school of adolescent irremediables.

During this latter time a fellow-headteacher in a primary school telephoned me exasperatedly about a young boy whom we had already discussed.

"Do you know, Bryn, the educational psychologist came to see him today, and his professional opinion was that 'the boy is not maladjusted enough yet' to come to your school. I ask you! **Enough**! YET!"

I relinquished my headship in the State Education System, and applied for a Heavy Goods Vehicle licence in order to earn myself a respectable and honorable livelihood, and not remain a party to an educational specialism which condoned the delayed treatment of child-distress.

I had a couple of years respite from the frustrations of the System. I knew about the impending publication of an educational Report which would surely change the face of the specialism which had become so galling to me. I bethought myself: I'll give them **one** last chance, I'll open a preventivist school for the distressed child. It will give the educational authorities and the school psychological services the opportunity to invest positively in the medially, perhaps even the minimally disturbed child, instead of the maximally disturbed youth. I drew up the brochure for the new type of school, delaying its printing till the publication of the Warnock Report in 1978, so confident was I that Its recommendations might be quoted to support my idea of a preventivist school. Sure enough they did. I duly quoted them, printed and circulated the brochure to educational authorities nationwide, and bought premises to meet the overwhelming response which I confidently expected would greet the excellent ideal of Preventivism . . .

After a month or two of quite ideal-blastingly underwhelming response, during which life went on and bills and red-notices smouldered in my in-tray, I devised a second, stark, no-nonsense brochure, offering to relieve the child placement administrators of hot potatoes burning **their** in-trays, and . . .

. . . Within another month or two I had begun to pay the salaries of our new staff, restore credit accounts with the local Gas, Electricity, and Water Boards, and pay for the groceries. Preventivism would have to wait. Perhaps in a year or two I can ask the Department of Education & Science for permission to accept 'referrals' from the parents of children unhappy at school . . . Perhaps **they** will be aware. I can dream of a time when the child under stress may refer him-or-her-self, however remote such an idea may seem as I write these words.

But for now I must adjust to the real world, must become wordly-wise. Je dois cesser de chercher le bonheur; je dois choisir mon propre malheur. And there are the needs of children to be served: it is not **their** fault that distress-signals were not read at an early stage.

Ah well, thanks for listening. I've had a good scratch. Feel better for that. The Post arrived a few minutes ago. Nowadays my life is governed by the Post. Gone are the old palmy days when I might expect, and budget with, a monthly salary-cheque. Now my life-hopes and life-fears are determined by big brown envelopes carrying the case-papers of newly-referred female youths under stress, and, later, small brown envelopes containing their fees.

What have we here then? A big brown envelope. Feels rather a **thick** big brown envelope. Fifteen years old . . . Withdrawn and under-achieving academically by the age of 10 . . . Temper tantrums during the first year of Secondary School . . . Query sexual abuse at age thirteen . . . Continual quarrelsomeness with other children leads to suspension and transfer to another school in town . . . At age fourteen strikes a teacher . . . Expulsion and admission to day Special School for the maladjusted in her area. Headteacher had grave misgivings about her admission, declaring that she needed to be away from home to be able to resolve her behavioural problem.

A paragraph or two of clever stuff about chronological-and-reading ages, number concepts, decomposition at three-figure level, laterality, and so forth. . . .

The brutal world outside the clinical cloisters intrudes again. Long summer holidays. Ran away to Manchester . . . Into care. Urgent referral for residential schooling.

H'm. Doesn't seem to have taken account of the opinion of her Infant-School teacher. Bet **she** noticed that tense, whining 5-year-old child, shrinking in her desk at the back of the class, chewing her pencil while the others worked.

I trudge gloomily back to my office, and the case papers thump massily on to my desk. I hear the clash of alligator jaws again. The swamp will have to wait.

Nuit de l'Enfer

We'd had a very peaceful week. The girls had been friendly and considerate towards Jane, and she had not absconded once. She had been to the dental clinic while Betty held her hand . . . well, actually her shoulders . . . and she was examined without swearing at the dentist once. Neil suggested that we celebrate Jane's growing maturity and the kindness of the others by taking six of them out to the cinema for the evening.

"And it'll give Tim and Betty a break for an evening. They've had a pretty hard time this last few weeks, and have been kept up till the early hours in the morning on several occasions".

"Yes, I'm sure they'll appreciate your thought for them. But is there a film which will be suitable for all the girls, with their diverse levels of concentration and maturity?"

"Aye, there's a film called **Rimbaud**, which is really gripping".

"Really?" I had my doubts. I recalled my own vagabond, if unpoetic, Rimbaud-stage of my early youth, when I had been sufficiently gripped by

Henry Miller's essay about the French poet to have seized and devoured Enid Starkie's bigraphy. But our girls . . . ? And then, of course, we realised that while I had **heard** the word 'Rimbaud', what Neil had **said** was 'Rambo'. I made a criticism of his French pronunciation, pointing out that he wasn't trilling his R's enough. He told me not to make personal remarks about his R's.

"I know it's a risk giving her back her shoes, but I've learned from you to play for high stakes".

"Yes, I agree. The sense of confidence she will achieve if she takes part in a normal community activity successfully is worth bidding for".

The peaceful week encourages me to change for bed at the early hour of 10.30.

The phone rings.

"Do you want the good news or the bad news first?"

"Let's have the good news first, Neil, in case you forget to tell it me while we're dealing with the bad".

"Right. Well, it was a really good evening. The girls thoroughly enjoyed **Rambo**, they behaved well during the ice-cream interval and they all . . . nearly all, thanked me for giving them such a grand evening".

"**Nea**rly all?"

"'Cept Jane".

"Ah".

"She was fine most of the time, A bit boisterous during the interval, but . . . "

"Did you say boisterous or boy-sterous?"

"Aye, you've guessed it, but, as I say, she was quite settled until we started to get into the car. She asked if she could sit in the front with me. I said I was sorry but I'd promised Ann because she was feeling sickly after her ice cream. So she shouts at me 'You're like me Step-Dad. He always lets me sister have the treats', and she walked off shouting and swearing. The others behaved calmly. They'd all got in, and Ann insisted on sitting in the back. We caught her up. Ann called to her to sit next to me, and I threw open the door. She shouted back, 'It's all right. You can have your favourite in the front next to you. I don't care. I didn't really want to sit there in the first place. Then she turned and walked back the way we had just driven and there was no way we could have caught her, or have persuaded her to get in the car in that mood, so I drove the others back to school as it was already late and phoned the police".

"Right, lad. Now I don't suppose you can push off to bed for a good night's kip?"

"We-l-l, I feel responsible for Jane".

"H'm. Thought so. Well, why don't you come and watch a video with me while the Panda-lads do their stuff. Can I persuade you to come and watch David Gower on song in the Oval Test?"

"No, I'll go back into Ripley. I can recognise her better than any police officer".

"Huh. Any police officer who isn't deaf will be able to recognise her to-night".

———— ————

Having lamented his early frost of that summer of 1985, I relished the bounteous yield of Gower's season of mellow fruitfulness, until the telephone rang again just before midnight.

"Hi, Betty".

"We've just had a call to say that Jane is on her way back with Neil in a police-car".

"And you'd like all officers on deck, I dare say".

"Might be helpful".

————————

It was a crestfallen Jane who followed a cheerful night-duty policeman and a tense Neil into the school.

Betty followed a mute and droop-headed figure down the corridor to the bedroom, while the gentlemen repaired to the withdrawing room, where they discussed the matters of the day. After a coffee P.C. Maurice was seen to the door.

Betty returned to the midnight coffee party rather troubled. "I've not known her like this before. She's just sitting there without a word, making no move to get ready for bed. I can usually get a smile of sorts from her, but not tonight, or rather", looking at her watch, "this morning. Shall I leave her a minute or two?"

"Might as well. Your continued attention may even delay her. Come and listen to Neil. He's just telling us what he's been up to".

"What a hell of a night! I spotted her as soon as I got to the Market place. Chatting to a couple of lads. So I drove straight to the Police Station, and two bobbies were just getting their Panda. They knew all about Jane, and told me to get into the back of their car. They drove off with a screaming of tyres, just like they do on Starsky & Hutch, and I banged my head on a door pillar. By the time I was upright again they were swerving into the Market Place and heading straight for Jane who was leaning against the chip-shop wall. The sergeant swung the front of the car obliquely almost against the wall and the young constable jumped out the passenger side and became the third wall of a triangle. The two lads looked frightened to death and scarpered as soon as they realised that they weren't the quarry. Jane turned to escape through the top of the triangle between the wall and the car, but by that time the sergeant was out of his side and had blocked that exit. I felt sorry for her. She was white. It was so sudden. I tried to get

89

out but neither of the handles at the back of the car would work. I suppose it's to stop prisoners escaping. So there I was, helplessly bouncing about from one door to the other trying to get out, and shouting behind the closed windows. But they couldn't hear me because Jane had started to favour them with her opinions about the police. I could hear *her* clearly enough, but I could only see their mouths opening and shutting as they presumably tried to reason with her. Then she spat at the car, and they grabbed her, one on each arm. They shoved her in the back with me, and I had to seize one flailing arm, or she'd have hit me, and the constable had hold of the other. Then, another breakneck dash through the streets to the Police Station. I could feel my hair standing on end. When we got there I don't know who felt worse, Jane or me. What a hell of a night.

"When we got inside the Station the sergeant spoke very sternly to Jane and told her that she was going to be charged with the offence of swearing at a Police Officer, and spitting at a Police car. Very serious, he said. He didn't know whether he could complete the formalities before he was due off duty at 2 o'clock. 'Take her to the Charging Room, Constable'. And poor Jane was led away. As soon as she was out of earshot, the sergeant relaxed his manner and winked at me. 'Give her 10 minutes and you can go and advise her, all quiet and unknown to us, that if she apologises nicely we *might* let her off, and perhaps you can get to bed before midnight'.

"So I did. And she did, very meekly. He spoke very gently to her, and she came back quiet as a lamb. But what a hell of a night".

But Neil's nuit de l'enfer was not over yet. The spirit of Rimbaud ruled us still.

Up the stairs we heard the decisive click-click of Jane's unmistakable gait. She pushed the door half-open so that we could hear her clearly, but couldn't see her at all.

"I've done it now. I'm doin' away wi' me sen".

"Yes, Love", Betty's voice gently responded. "Come and kiss me goodnight".

"No, you can't get round me any more. I've tooken 12 tablets". (J'ai avalé une gorgée de poison: Rimbaud again).

"Yes, duck. Well, you'll sleep soundly then, won't you?"

"An' you can tell me mum and dad that they'll never be troubled wiv me again". (Parent, vous avez fait mon malheur). "They'll never 'ave to stay up late at night again waitin' for me, or come to the Police Station to pick me up and gi' me a good beltin'".

Jane came into view round the door, and had evidently intended to go into further detail, but the memory of her younger and more vulnerable self arrested her. Her mouth remained open wordlessly. Her eyes stared without focus. She stumbled and clasped the door more tightly, and began blinking as if to prompt tears, too ready and profuse in the past, to flow ⌐ freely now. (La violence du venin tord mes membres, me rend difforme, me terrasse . . . je ne puis pleurer).

"But Jane", the headmaster interposed calmingly, "you haven't had a good belting tonight, and you're not going to get one". I warmed to a familiar thesis. What these abused girls need is to be assured that there will be no retribution. "And we are as your parents now", I purred, "We are going to **care** for you from now on . . . "

Jane raised her head again.

"An' **you** can shut up for a start. I've 'ad a **belly**ful of you tonight. I'm up to 'ere with **you**".

She burst into the room, and only I, from my position facing the door, could see her. The others remained unmoved and unmoving as Jane continued her tirade, but my attention became fixed on her mouth. I was deaf to her words, but watched her moving lips. They were bright red, as were her gums, tongue and teeth. What had the crazed child done? She needs a hospital. Where's the phone?

"Just stay where you are, Bryn. Don't touch me".

Had she put a bit of glass in her mouth?

"If you lay a finger on me I'll jump outa that winder".

Perhaps it was powdered glass. (Les entrailles me brulent . . . Un homme qui veut se mutiler est bien damné, n'est ce pas?) Would an ordinary emetic work with powdered glass?

"Where's the tablet bottle, Jane?"

"Oh, so you think I've not really swallowed any, do you? You think I'm not really serious about killin' me sen, do you? Well, here's me proof", she unclenched a tight fist, and, as the door swung to behind her, little empty plastic sachets fluttered to the floor.

From the stairs, as she distanced herself further from the theatre of her dramatic declaration, we heard, diminuendo, "I'm going to me own room where I can die in peace and quiet".

Betty eased her attractive ampleness out of her chair impassively, "I'll come and lay you out then, me duck". As she opened the door she bent casually and picked up one of the sachets. She stiffened suddenly, took in her breath sharply, and exclaimed, "Oh my God", and rushed out of the room.

Neil, Tim and I sat transfixed, looking at each other helplessly. Neil breathed quietly, "What a hell of a night". I rose to follow Betty.

The door opened, and all three gazes switched to Betty's face peering round it mischieveously, "Don't look so worried, Bryn. We left her rather a long time alone in the Waiting-Room this morning while I talked to the dentist". She brought the sachet up to reading distance from her eyes: "Dental plaque tablets".

Collapse of Stout Party and Elderly Party — helplessly into each other's arms!

Christmas Spirit

I had called to meet Rachel in her Wiltshire home in anticipation of her admission to school in the near future.

I had expected 20 minutes or so of nervous cordiality from my hosts while I bumbled away about what 15-year-old Rachel might prepare herself to meet at her new school. But Rachel, her mother, and I, talked the sun down over the horizon in friendly and open conversation.

Rachel made careful enquiry about the manners and members of the community and expressed herself willing to come. But . . . there seemed to be some reservation. I encouraged her candour about any misgivings she might have.

"Well, I think you ought to know that I'm a right bitch underneath". She eyed me anxiously, as if I might withdraw my offer.

I assumed a shocked facial expression, and explained that we didn't have bitches at our school: we usually had girls who, if they cared to tell us, had been grossly victimised at school, had been betrayed by ill-chosen friends, and were totally innocent of all the false allegations which had been brought against them. In short, and altering my expression, it was a rare pleasure to meet someone who was prepared to be honest about herself so early in our acquaintance. In fact, although I had come to interview her for a place after Christmas, two months hence, since she had declared herself a bitch, might I offer her a place to be taken up the following week? She accepted laughingly, and, taking our leave at the front door, she reminded me to be sure to make the prompt arrangements for her admission.

Jessie, from the same county, came for interview several weeks later. Her mother, she and I went straight to the Common Room for a talk together.

After a few introductory remarks by me, I paused, looked hard at the floor, then addressed myself to the parent.

"Well, Mrs. Jeffries, I have interviewed your daughter, and should be glad to offer her a place at our school".

A moment of confusion. A glance from me to Jessie and back again. "But, Mr. Purdy . . . I didn't think you'd had time to talk with her".

"I haven't, but I've seen her smile".

Jessie and Rachel roomed together, and it was my pleasure to listen to their gentle Southlands brogue as I helped them rearrange the furniture to their liking, while the bud of their acquaintance bloomed into friendship.

Quick blooming, however, may betoken early fading, horticulturally and in human relationships.

Not a fortnight later, the day before the end of the Autumn Term, and on the day of the Christmas Dinner and Party, the two girls were less than rapturous about their new-found friendship.

Jessie was up and dressed unusually early, and asked me for a private talk. She explained that things were not working out in the bedroom. The two girls were not getting on. She asked if she might move into another bedroom. But, curiously and exceptionally, not a word **against** Rachel. I consented to the move.

Rachel stayed in bed, feigning sleep, unusually late.

Downstairs, Pat's successor, her friend and fellow-churchwoman, Lesley, was marshalling her small volunteer kitchen militia. Assorted vegetable peel was bundled and discarded, gas jets were flaring, pots were bubbling, tables were being set and festooned.

Thoughtlessly, I had popped in for a chat. In my personal life I abjure as far as possible all ritual, and consider the celebration of christmas memorable only for the wondrous and pacific Event which it prompted between the German and the English soldiers on the Western Front in 1914. The momentum of the seasonal festivities is initiated and sustained by other staff than me. Lesley was her usual friendly and welcoming self, but . . .

"I'll get out of your way. I wouldn't like to have your job today, Lesley".

"I wouldn't like yours, Bryn — ever".

Jessie broached me again for a further word. Her concern now is that she might hurt Rachel's feelings by the bedroom move.

I suggested that she sleep at a Befriender's overnight, thus contriving neither to spend the night in Rachel's company nor to offend her. She seemed pleased at this resolution of the problem.

I expressed my appreciation that, instead of trying to blast her way through the problem by sheer wilfulness, she had chosen to talk her way round it. She smiled. My intuition had been right: the verbal interview had been unnecessary.

I broached Rachel, kneeling by her bedside the closer to address her turned back and tousled hair.

"I've been in to see you several times over the last couple of hours, my dear. You seemed to be asleep, so I didn't wish to wake you, even though I conjectured that you were pretending to be asleep. I did not wish to

93

intrude on you. If you're feeling ill, I'm sorry: if you're feeling hurt, I'd like to comfort you. Can I help?"

A pause. I waited stilly.

A thin, unfamiliar voice emerged from the bedclothes. "No thanks. I feel ill. Please tell the others not to come and disturb me".

An aroma compounded of turkey, roast potatoes and plum pudding permeated the building, wafted by the frequent opening-and-closing of the kitchen door by the curious and the hungry.

I entered Rachel's room once more to find her lying in the same position. I expected that not having had breakfast and the prospect of a square — not to say cuboid — meal would have a positive effect on Rachel's everready appetite and susceptible palate. I felt sure that her digestion was willing, but her feelings were wounded.

The Christmas dinner passed off very successfully, both gastronomically and in terms of seasonal spirit — but with one empty chair.

After she had denied herself the pleasures of the table, Rachel dressed herself and sought me out where I was on my knees adjusting the television.

"Hi, Rachel. Hope you're feeling better now".

"Not really. I gotta see you, Bryn. I've decided I can't sleep in the same bedroom as Jessie".

"I'm sorry to hear that, Rachel. I know that you've taken several hours to arrive at the decision, so I won't seek to persuade you otherwise, but would it help to talk it over with anyone?"

"I just 'ad a long talk with Meg, so I don't need to, thanks. Jessie and me, we just . . ."

She halted as Jessie herself came through the door and crossed to the nearest chair with the delicate and careful tread of the cat who has found its prey — cornered. "I 'ope you don't mind me joinin' you — as you were talking about me".

I found myself equidistant between the two antagonists, and eased myself from my knees to my haunches the more readily to wicket-keep any wild deliveries from either side. The two girls sat straight-backed, the frosted-glass of their eyes averted from each other.

"We weren't actually talking about you, Jess. Rachel was just asking me if she could change her room . . ."

"I can answer, Bryn, thank you", said Rachel regaining her tongue if not her composure. "I wuz tellin' Bryn that we d-don't get on t-together, like we used to". A slight stammer indicated her anxiety.

94

"An' I bin tellin' Bryn the same thing meself. I ain't said nothin' 'gainst you, Rachel, you can a-as' Bryn. I just want to move out that bedroom".

"That's right, Jessie: she didn't say a word against you . . . And would you mind if I told Rachel of our conversation this morning. I think it might reassure her . . . "

"No thanks. I can tell 'er meself. But first I'd just like to 'pologise for what I said to you las' night, Rachel, after lights-out".

"'S all right. I deserved it really. I shouldn't 've snapped at you . . . I'm sorry for snappin' at you".

I relaxed from haunched to seated position against the wall and watched the two girls over the next few minutes discard stilettoes in favour of a school-girl pillow-fight of laughing insults. The antagonism of the night before rehearsed, probably to the very words, but seen through the refracting glass of humour.

"'F only you didn't spend so much time in front of that dressin'-table mirror . . . "

"'F only **you** didn't leave your clothes all over the floor . . . "

"You're **vain**, tha's what you are".

"An' you're an untidy slut: that's what **you** are".

Breathless and bright-eyed, and now totally reconciled, they turned their joint pillow-attack on their adult spectator, who sat enthralled at what he feared would be feathers-flying transpiring to be the wafting of soft down.

"'Course I still love you. It's all the fault of that room. It's too small!"

"It's all Bryn's fault for puttin' us in there".

"Yes, it's all your fault, Bryn".

"But what about that big bedroom. That'd suit us foine. Shall we move in there together?"

"Yes, that's a **lovely** room. Can we move in there, Bryn?"

"'Course we can. Bryn'll let us, won't you, Bryn".

"Let's go and look at it now".

And, arm-in-arm they marched off to their new room, leaving me to marvel at how die sanften Flügel of the Christmas Spirit had waved over and blessed our small community.

"Come **on**, Bryn. We need some help to move this wardrobe".

A Policeman's Lot

It was the year of Torville-and-Dean's great triumph on the television sets of the world, and I had just entered the ice-drome where they had learned their first faltering steps. The six girls I was accompanying were changing into their ice-skates. During the lunch hour the rink is closed to the general public to give the hard-core competitors freedom to practice more formal figure-skating.

I stroll easefully round the perimeter, outside the waist-high barrier, and my eyes lightly take in the dozen or so skaters — when they suddenly focus on a familiar duo: I was the solitary spectator that December day in Nottingham of the World Champions, who had been the cynosure of a myriad eyes during the past few months.

I stare bemusedly as the small screen suddenly enlarges and makes alive the two figures, gracefully gyrating to the voice of the tinny loudspeakers. I trip. The music stops, and the dance suddenly twirls to a close. I look down at the sprung-apart connections of the audio-cable. Headmaster Clouseau has done it again. I look up, and to my dismay, discover Ex-Police Constable Dean skating directly for me. I mumble my apologies when, within moments, he is within earshot. He smiles, "Oh, don't let that bother you. We were just finishing anyway", Gracious as well as graceful.

I turn my mind to less tractable embarrassments. Of course, I had misgivings about bringing Jane in the first place. Her baulking of the early jump after the cinema in the small town of Ripley was not a distant memory. But still, she had managed the Beecher's Brook of Birmingham City Centre, albeit after a solitary canter, so let her continue her round in Nottingham. The trouble with our Jane is that one is torn between a continuous precipice horror that she may collapse into childish irrationality and compound her sense of failure, and that she may gain confidence by succeeding at something. One has to take the risk, I feel.

On our way into the City Centre I had given my poor contused ear-drums momentary relief from the latest vocal effusions of **Wham**!, and had explained to the other girls, necessarily in her hearing of course, that no one was to tell Jane to do **any**thing, under **any** circumstances. She might only be coaxed, gentled into any course of action, but that sharpness of tone would certainly cause her to panic.

The car was stopped at traffic lights, and each girl gravely nodded her understanding of my counsel in response to my glance to them individually.

Jane has justified my optimism as she hand-hauls herself round the edge of the first quadrant of the rink, chortling and squealing her glee. I walk round the outside of the barrier, keeping pace but unnoticed, when suddenly the warm flow of her confidence cools, ices over, then freezes solid. Like another Dumbo, made to feel different from the other children from birth, unaccustomed to success, she had faltered in mid-flight. I offer her the feather of my voice. She is too terrified to accept it, or even hear my offer, and continues to plummet. The other birds, sensing her anxiety, fly in to coo encouragingly. Minutes pass, and helplessly they take wing again. She stands, 'effrayée' by her own personal 'gouffre'. I cajole, urge, encourage. It is strange not to meet the fierce heat of the flame-thrower of her counter-argument: more, she allows herself to be **seen**, not head-hung but full-face, at her most defenceless, stuttering her tearfulness through clenched teeth. I point out the next exit from the rink only 20 feet away. "If only . . . . . . And you needn't come on the ice again". Tourist skaters rubber-neck by, and, to my dismayed imagination, see only a manifestly pubescent girl distressed by the over-familiar attentions of a middle-aged man. It's happening all the time. You read about it in the newspapers. I walk off ruefully. Some use my 20 years experience with, and insight into, disturbed children. But she is still my responsibility. What can I **do**? Should I bodily haul her over the barrier? **Could** I? No, she is too big and . . . pubescent. But I might collect the other five girls and effect it between us. I turn on my heel and begin to walk purposefully back — when Jane sweeps past me squealing and radiant-faced. "Come on, Bryn". I make a second volte-face, (and, echoing the schoolboy howler, 'make a revolting face' at the contrariness of adolescent girl).

A fast stride keeps me abreast with Jane, joyous in her new-found skill, demonstrating once again how fast she can learn.

Then I am forgotten, and I can share my attention, chocolate, peanuts, and encouragement among the others more equally, or according to need.

I stroll around the rink with slowly measured tread, like a policeman at a cricket match, thinking what a damn fine job **this** is. Always fancied being the policeman on duty at a cricket match. Strolling round, watching the play from different vantage points, sharing in the crowd's enjoyment of the spectacle. Being paid for it.

. . . When my professional antennae begin to tremor. What is the matter? There is Eve, who is holding a Primary School child by each hand, teaching them to skate. O.K. there. One. There is Jessie, whose bright petals and slender alluring stem had attracted several ice-rink drones to circle round her. She can protect her pollen from that swarm. Two. And there are Lorraine and Chris, trying to get the helplessly laughing Sonia on her feet again. Five. But Jane! Where is Jane? Under corrugated brows my narrowed eyes scan the twirling figures, once . . . twice. Nowhere to be seen. In unmeasured scamper I dash down the nearest short staircase which leads to the pedestrian circuit outside the ice rink itself. Striding round half the perimeter, up and down two more staircases, I become aware of the heavy roar of Jane's flame-thrower voice. I am drawing near enough for the words to become dismayingly intelligible.

"That fookin' bitch . . . Wait till I get me 'ands on 'er . . ."

I turn the corner of the latest staircase to be met with the full blast of her invective. She is standing half-way up, and has attracted a small group of listeners-on. But she was waiting for me, has been expecting me. In acknowledgment of my presence she turns down the volume of her flame-thrower, the more accurately and powerfully to jet what she has to say directly at me.

"An' let me tell you, Bryn", she hisses, "**you**'d be'er keep 'er ou' **my** way, or, I'm warnin' you, she's **dead**".

"Yes, yes, my dear. Who is she?"

"What do you mean, 'Who is she?'" as if I hadn't been listening. "An' I keep tellin' you, I'm **not** your dear: I'm not **your** . . . **any**thin'".

"Yes, lo . . . Yes, Jane, but who are you talking about?"

"'**Er**, of course. That, that . . ." Unhappily Jane isn't lost for flames, and, after an explosive branding of 'her' lineage, Jane proceeded to cauterise 'her' character and personal attributes, expletively, extensively, in detail, and wholly destructively. Happily she ended her incendiary tirade with the clue I had been searching for among the charred embers of her description: ". . . that Jessie!"

"Ah! **Jes**sie — you're talking about Jessie". She skewers me with her eyes, and opens her mouth, so I quickly add, "What has she done to you? What has Jessie **done**?"

"What has she done? What has she DONE?", as if she'd just told me. She was drawing a deep breath, and I quickly interpose questions.

"Has she **said** something? Is it those boys?"

"Boys?" she said, genuinely puzzled, staring at me hard.

The staircase audience had pressed closer to hear her lowered voice. Jane is oblivious to them, even if I am not, and the points of her runaway mind have been switched to another track by this new word.

"Boys. I 'ate boys. I 'ate all men. All men are bastards". The audience cranes closer still and, being largely young and female, seem to communicate their fellow-feeling. "An' the biggest bastard o' the lo' is my step-dad".

I hear a background titter and response.

"'E can't be 'er dad then. Must be . . ."

"mMm".

Jane seems to have forgotten about Jessie now, and is setting her sights on her more customary target, as her voice rises.

"At least I **thought** 'e was the biggest bastard till I met **you**".

Again the counterpoint to this dramatic monologue was heard in the background.

"I saw 'im chattin' up a few other young gels out there, givin' 'em sweets an' suchlike".

"mmMmm".

To be subject to Jane's contumely in private was uncomfortable enough, but before a now small and potentially grandstand audience . . . I seek again a rational object to her feelings of hostility.

"Can you remember what it was that Jessie did or said to upset you. I'm sure she didn't mean . . . "

"Jessie". And her voice softens from a hiss to a whisper, as the events of the afternoon trigger off memories of years ago. "Jessie . . . She tol' me that she loved me . . . that she would be my best friend . . ." My unwitting shaft of a question had targetted, and poor Jane stands transfixed now by acute emotional pain as earlier she had been frozen by panic. Her eyes are filled with tears. I stretch out my hand towards her. Is **this** the moment of truth for which I had been waiting for so many months? Dare I touch her? My hand settles gently on her white knuckles as they grip the metal stair-rail. If only she can allow herself to be comforted . . .

Her eyes are fixed on the middle distance, her mind lost in her distant past. Jane suddenly blinks the tears out of her eyes, and perceives the danger which immediately threatens her. She snatches her hand away from me so suddenly that she unbalances herself on the fins of her skates, and she lies looking up at me terrorstruck, as now I stand over her, as if it were I who had engineered her downfall.

Blown about on the sea of her emotions, from acute distress, through terror, and now to anger, she snatches at the laces of her shoes with frenzied fingers. "Bloody skates". She wrenches one off, and the gleaming blade which now lies uppermost in her hand buffets her compassless mind once more in another direction, but powered by the same emotion of molten anger. "Wait till I ge' me 'ands on 'er. I'll tear 'er to bits". The brandished bluntness of metal glints dully in the artificial half-light. "She'll 'ave no flesh on 'er bones by the time I've done cuttin' 'er up".

She limps ungainly off round the outer perimeter, broadswording the skate from side to side.

What to do now? On my past record, I had perhaps better lay aside any strategy based on influencing a more rational attitude in Jane.

No, I would settle for protecting Jessie, perhaps securing her alliance in somehow conciliating Jane. No again. Jessie's a gril after all, and has been in attendance at the school only as many weeks as Jane has been months. She has had strained and splintering relationships in **her** past as well, no doubt. No, my best hope was for Jane to abscond, and get lost in Nottingham; for me to take the others home to safety, and to return this evening when some Police Station telephones me.

As I emerge indeterminately on to rink-level, I bethink myself of my serene constabulary tread of 10 minutes ago. Now I find myself a one-man riot-squad, unarmed, without radio contact with headquarters, and with no hope of reinforcements. Not a happy lot!

Ah, there's Jessie over at the other side of the rink, sunning herself, I see, among a buzz of male admiration. Even as I puff round, my mind is engaged at a deeper level with the consolatory thought that Jane **can** be distressed by a fractured relationship, where hitherto she has been exercised only by her effort to keep us all at bay. It has taken a new girl to get beneath her guard. The long-term prospect looks brighter.

"Hi, Bryn".

"Hi, Jessie. Hi, Steve: it **is** Steve, isn't it? Thought I remembered you from a week or two ago. No, Alison isn't here to-day. Hi, Garry, nice to meet you.

"Now, Jess, I must have a word. One of the other girls feels she has some grievance against you, and I'd like you to remain calm while we try to sort things out. I'm sure there's been some misunderstanding . . . "

Suddenly Jessie's mobile and well-formed features set concrete-hard, and the lilting twang of her voice becomes a rasp. "Oh, yeh — and what'm I s'posed t'ave done, then? That's the trouble wi' this school. Everyone's always gossipin' 'bout someone else. You can't lead your life wi'out some busybody stickin' their nose in. Come on, what 'ave I done then? Oo's bin complainin' 'bout me? I'll go an' 'sort it out' now: leastways, sort *'er* out".

She swings round to face the ice, hands gripping the rail behind her, and immediately spots a chain of one, two, three, four, red-cheeked, laughing, careening, totally absorbed girl-skaters. That leaves . . .

"*Jane*. Where's Jane?" She whirls on me. "Where's Jane? It's Jane, i'n' it? Why didn't you tell me it wuz Jane?"

I had not told her anything, for fear of fuelling the flames.

"I gotta find 'er".

Do I perceive a softening of tone?

"You see, she's 'ad a 'ell-uva life. She wuz tellin' me laas' ni'".

"You're right, she's had a very unhappy childhood . . . "

"I promised to be 'er friend. I'd best go-find 'er".

. . . "and at the moment she's in an unstable frame of mind, indeed, she's very . . . No, Jess. *NO*, Let's go together".

But even now Jessie is half-way over the rink, gliding lissomly to the exit-staircase at the far end.

I look helplessly after: poor Jessie knows not what a convergence of the twain awaits her across the ice.

I take my leave abruptly of the lads, and set of at a constabularly double, just fast enough to arrive at the scene of the likely affray, consistent with not causing a breach of the peace among the innocent members of the public through whom I nimbly zig-zag. We haven't had any trouble with the staff of the Ice Rink since out first visit, over five years ago, when Deirde felled their doorman with a sharp kick to each ankle.

I dart down a staircase and do a further circuit at an increased speed, more military than constabulary. No one. I pause, lean against a wall and listen. For a moment or two my ears are filled with the sound of my own stertor. Nothing. Only distant, echoing, youthful jocundity. Perhaps she has absconded after all. My luck's changing. To the exit at a less frantic pace. No one in the entrance hall. But do I not see two familiar forms as I pad past the changing-room?

I put my head round the door to find the girls seated next to each other, Jane's boot lying harmlessly on the floor. Jessie's arm is around Jane, her hand patting her shoulder reassuringly, talking to her so softly that I cannot hear the words. Jane's beatifically happy smile and long, slow nodding were conversational response enough. Jane's unremitting hostility to me personally, day in, week out, for three grinding months might have caused me despair for her future, but the happiness in her face now suggests that she had some good childhood experience on which we can build.

We? Where do *I* come into it? I have been offering Jane my friendship now for nearly a whole school term, apparently quite unavailingly, and this chit of a girl comes along, and has immediate access to her affections.

It may simply be personal, or it may be because I am, as it were, a uniformed adult, however much I may seek to operate in plainclothes. I suppose my rôle is that of the policeman on the beat: a patrolling presence and occasional riot-control.

Anyway, there's no need to risk spoiling the atmosphere here by an unnecessary showing of the uniform. I may have performed some function by drawing the fire of Jane's antagonism. I can now leave her to this latest recruit to the Rowen House Irregulars, who may go where no adult can safely follow.

I resume my patrol of the ice rink.

Left, Right. Left, Right. Left, Right.

Glance at my watch. Near the end of my shift. Quick gesture to one of the Irregulars, who swerves round to tell the others that we must go now if we are to miss rush-hour traffic. Cheery wave of acknowledgement from several of them. Nice kids. Nice friendly patch I've got.

Shoulders squared. Hands clasped behind my back.

Left   Right   Left   Right   Left   Right

Nothing much to record in the Logbook today.

A Paternal Gift

"So what you're saying, Bryn, is that you'll give us what we want?"

"No, I didn't exactly say that, Jessie. What I said was that our aim is to make each girl happy . . . I mean **help** each girl to **become** happy — you can't **make** people happy, can you — in her own way. We try to run the school in such a way that it is continually changing to meet the needs of each individual girl who forms part of our community . . ."

Jessie anticipates a lecture, and interjects, "No what I mean is, you said to Rachel that if she wanted anything she only had to write you a note for it".

"Er, yes . . . I did. I said that if she particularly likes Marmite she could write a note to remind us to buy it from the Cash & Carry. You can write a note for anything . . . reasonable".

"Oh, I see".

A few minutes later a slip of paper fluttered on to my desk.

> Dear Bryn   22.1.86.
>   Please could you buy me a fountain pen Please for
> my schoolwork and if I go to college.
>   Thankyou
>   Jessie

Jessie had arranged to go and stay the week-end with her father and his second wife. She had not seen him for nearly a year and her increased stability of behaviour had encouraged us to hope that there might be some reconciliation between them.

We parked in town far from the Station, and I responded to Emma's puzzled eyes by explaining that I needed to do some shopping.
"Will you come for company?"
"Sure".
"Good, because I have an obligation to fulfil towards you . . . No, turn here, into the stationer's shop. Do you remember you asked for a pen the other day? Well, it's the kind of request I'm happy to respond to. I'd like you to choose a fountain pen to help you to go to college. You can choose one up to the value of . . . say £5".
"Oh, no, Bryn", and her Southlands drawl was in contrast to the shortened vowels of the murmur in the shop around us. "Oi don't want a **fa-ancy** one . . . "
After a few minutes' deliberation, "Oi'll 'ave tha-at one".
"Are you sure", noting the price of £1.99 "You can choose another if you wish".
"No, that'll suit me foine".
"Put it on the school account, please, Les. Thank you".
As we drove to the station, I wished her all the best for her academic career, and hoped that the pen might be a starting-point for her.
" . . . You have a brain that could well take you into Further Education of some sort. I know you've had a stressed life this last few years but you have a chance now of reversing events. 'Today is the first day of the rest of your life' . . .
"Oh, there's one further thing I must add. The school has given you a pen, in response to your request. We make reasonable gifts to any girl who has the initiative to ask for something, but we always ask the girl not to mention it to the others. I don't want **everyone** to ask for a pen, just because you have.
"Oi gedit, Bryn. 'F anyone a-asks me I'll say me Da-ad give it me over the weekend".

On Monday afternoon I came upon a morose Jessie sitting at her dressing table, chin on clenched fist, finding no solace in her attractive features in the mirror.
"Hi, Jess. Didn't know you were back. Had a good . . . No . . . sorry, Silly question . . . Sorry . . . "
Rachel was busying herself on her side of the room. "Don't a-ask 'er Bryn. She's 'ad a **terr**'ble time".
"I'm sorry, Jessie. I was **so** hopeful about the week-end with your dad. May I ask where things went wrong?"
"Everythin'. Jus' **ev**erythin'".

"Sorry. And sorry for finding nothing more useful to say than 'sorry'. Was there nothing in the 48 hours that was positive, that we can work on for the future?"

Jessie did not turn her head, but her eyes, moist with unshed tears, found mine in the mirror's reflection. Her features twitched into a smile, but it did not reach her eyes, which continued to hold mine, recognising my concern. She would like to have comforted me in my disappointment.

Suddenly, she became all quick movement, searching in the recesses of her week-end bag.

"There **wuz one** good thing Bryn". She held up her new pen, eyes still glistening, but mischievously now, and Rachel came to look too.

"Oi got a presen' off me da-ad".

God's Excuse : a Theological Colloquy

" . . . And I told her, Bryn, that she **need**n't become a mother at 15, but that there are perfectly reasonable and honourable ways . . ."

(pianissimo) "Can I 'ave a baff, Tim?"

"I do agree with you, Tim. When we had our first few pregnancies here I used to pussyfoot about the problem, being sublimely non-directional . . .

(crescendo) "Can I 'ave a baff, Tim?"

(Tim and I were unwise to have begun a serious conversation in open ground, without the cover afforded by a closed door against marauding grils. So often had the chalice of adult communion been dashed from our lips).

" . . . But her mother has told her, Bryn, that it's God's decision that she have a baby, and she has no right to go against God".

(forte) "Can I 'ave a **baff** Tim?"

"**How** many times do I have to **tell** you, Sarah, that you must **wait** until people have finished talking till you say your piece . . . Now where were we, Tim?" I looked at him helplessly, trying to retrieve the thread of conversation which the sharpness of my tone had cut.

Pause

(sotto voce) "Can I 'ave a baff, Tim . . . please?"

Tim looked from my glazed eyes and goldfish mouth, and within a few athletic strides and less seconds, had returned with a plastic phial of bath lotion.

"Now just be careful not to spill it this time, Sarah, and if you run too much water into the bath, you'll have to mop it up your**self** this time".

(dolcissimo) "Thank you, Tim".

"Yes, you were saying how sublimely non-directional you were . . . "

"Ah, yes . . . but now I just advise the occassional pregnant girl that we have that the odds are stacked heavily against the adolescent mother".

"Yes, but what chance has even your word against the dictum of God? Not that I **blame** God".

"No, no, nor I".

And for a minute or two we shadow-talked, each careful not to offend the sensibilities of the other, for this was a subject we hadn't broached during the two years of our colleagueship. Then the barques of our two minds drew near on the halcyon sea of consent: the one nurtured in one of the ancient universities and steeped in the cultures of the two classic and three modern languages; the other which had pursued the study of the philosophia perennialis through the **Tao**, the **Gita**, and the works of Eckhardt, William Law, Miguel de Unamuno, and Richard Jefferies. The prows of the two vessels converged, met, and treasures were exchanged.

"But I would have you know, Bryn, that some of my best friends are Christians".

"And, for my part, during my youth I felt rather uncomfortable with certain of my elders because I was not a Believer in This or That. I felt with Woody Allen, when he declared to his proselytising companion, 'To you, I'm an Atheist: to God, I'm a member of His loyal opposition'".

. . . "And have you heard of the historian, Bryn, whom Napoleon appointed to write the complete History of the World. When it was completed he asked him why it contained no mention of God. The historian replied, "Je ne voyais pas la nécessité".

"Yes, I appreciate the rationalist, almost pedestrian, note struck by that answer, Tim, but I respond to Richard Jeffries' higher call for a 'soul-emotion' beyond merely petitionary prayer and for an awareness of the godhead outside what mankind has created for himself over the aeons in his 'gods' and now his 'God'. A high-water mark of resigned but reverent agnosticism is a poem by Antonio Machado, who recalls his dream-state of the night before, in which he likens his soul-emotion to a mountain spring from an unknown source, to a hive whose bees are creating sweet soul-honey from an uncomprehended sadness in the past and, in the penultimate, to

>. . un ardiente sol que lucía
>dentro de mi corazón.
>Era ardiente porque daba
>calores de rojo hogar,
>y era sol porque alumbraba
>y porque hacía llorar.

The Believer would, of course, consider that such sublime feeling could come only from God, but Machado perorates his poem with the speculation that

>Last night as I lay sleeping, I dreamt, O blessed illusion,
>That it was God whom I held within my Heart.

An **illusion** that God exists, yes, but a **blessed**, a holy, illusion; a fine balance between theolatry and scepticism".

"Splendid. Splendid. The pain for the believer in an omnipotent God is the need to **blame** Him for Man's crassnesses, as poor Elgar did during the First World War, when he railed against God for harming his beloved horses. Stendhal's answer to that plaint was, 'God's only excuse is that He doesn't exist'. Or was it Flaubert?"

But our sea-idyll was interrupted not by the Song of the Sirens but by the shrill of the Harpies.

(From the bathroom) Tim . . . *(crescendo)* Tim . . . "

"No . . . Stendhal, I feel sure . . . "

"TIM"

" . . . but I'd better go". Tim sped downstairs to discover what disaster had befallen Sarah, leaving his conversational partner in a state of coitus interruptus mentis. And so, Timothy Shadbolt, Magister Artium Oxoniensis and Housefather, who so loves his fellow-creatures that he forbears to eat them, and who so loves his fellow-humans that he had foregone the more elegant and congenial society to be found among the dreaming spires to consort with and succour the denizens of the concrete jungle of our society, rushed to the aid of a raucous, barely literate, ill-coordinated 12-year-old child.

(Fortissimo) "T-i-i-m"

"Now, Sarah, what's the matter?"

(Agitato) "Oh, you're 'ere". (Then *piangevole*) "There's a spider in me baff."

"Yes. And what's the matter?"

"There's a spider in me baff. Kill it"

"Ah, I don't think that's necessary. I'll just pick it up and take it outside".

(staccato) "No. No. Kill it, **Kill** it",

(soave) "No, No. There's no need to kill a spider just because it wants to share your bath". (And to think that at this moment Tim might be pouring coffee preparatory to a seminar with some eager student about his beloved Wittgenstein, against the backdrop of rich-hued wainscotting and, through the windows, greensward in the cloisters).

"Yes you do. You kill spiders in de baff". Sarah had shifted the ground of her argument from the particular to the general, and Tim was nothing loth to engage in more philosophical discourse, addressing himself, as always, to the level of understanding of his interlocutor.

"But **why**, Sarah? Why should you **want** to kill spiders?" Tim is wonderfully persuasive, and his gentle rationality is making Sarah waver, so he essays a higher emotional pitch, addressed to the Infant School classroom, if not the nursery. "Why should you want to kill spiders which . . . God has put on this earth?"

There is a long thoughtful silence while Sarah gives due consideration to the escalating reason of Tim's latest submission, before she delivers a coup-de-marteau argument which ends this unequal colloquy.

"Well . . . God shouldn't put spiders in me baff".

From Mansfield to Bournemouth

It is over nine months since Jane went 'to Mansfield': 9 months, 3 foster parents, 2 'fiancés' killed on motor bikes, one phantom pregnancy, and, as recorded in **Nuit de L'Enfer**, one attempted suicide.

So, as life was becoming rather dull for her, she decided to abscond again the week-end after she had arrived at her latest Foster Parents. Rumour had it that she had been sighted in Birmingham City Centre, but, anyway, she has turned up safe and sound.

We sit together on the carpet of the sitting-room, holding hands gently, she replying shyly to my enquiries about her welfare, as if she had just returned from her first term at Finishing School.

"And, if you'll allow me to ask you, our dear Jane, where have you been for the past month? If you care to tell me, that is. Only we have been concerned about you".

"No, I don't mind tellin' y'. I felt I needed a holiday, so I went to Wales". Her holiday must have done her good, for she smiled at me and looked at me as she spoke. "I got some fren's there, an' Oi stayed wiv 'em".

"And how did you manage for money?"

"Oi did odd jobs for me fren's, loike. It was a sea-side place, y'see".

"Oh, Yes. And where abouts was it in Wales?"

"Bournemuff".

"Bournemouth!" I exclaimed, as the Janus-signposts of Mansfield and Mancester flashed on the retina of my memory. "But Bournemouth's in . . . " Then more gently. "I wonder if you mean Barmouth?"

"Ah, that's it" smiling at me easily, "it must have been Barmuff".

Messering About

I have declared in the Caveat that it was never my intention to sensationalise the daily life of a school for young women under stress, that I would eschew the merely eventful, that my aim was to observe the flickering light of highly-charged young female character shining through the prism of dramatic incident.

However, the melodramatic has its place in our daily life, and, as such, deserves to be catalogued, but, as here, may be disposed of briefly — indeed, thanks to the admirable compendiousness of the German language, in a single word.

Arrived in my office one morning, I found a piece of paper sellotaped to my desk above the drawers with the legend written in Tim's handwriting,

Die scharfen Messer sind darunter

I ingested the information and, knowing that its message was safely inscrutable to most eyes, and supposing that I might be more fully apprised in due course, I left the note where Tim had seen fit to put it, simply adding

Danke

Several days passed, however, without further elucidation so, knowing that Lesley would begin to query the absence of her kitchen knives, I appended to the foregoing the question

Aber warum?

The following morning the whole incident stood starkly resumed:

Die scharfen Messer sind darunter
Danke
Aber Warum?
Selbstmordspiel

Mootivation

Late this afternoon a visitor arrived at school. Gordon is a second cousin of a scion of my family which was grafted to Australia a generation or two ago. He comes not only as a relative but as a fellow-professional, for he is on a sabbatical year from the headmastership of a large, rural, secondary school.

One of the girls has shown him round the school, and he has been the centre of a chorus of excited questions about himself and his homeland.

He has been kind enough to invite us out to a restaurant for the evening meal, and he notes with some surprise that I have left my 'forwarding' telephone number with the staff at school.

"You don't expect to be called during the next couple of hours do you, Bryn?"

"I expect nothing until it has happened, but I try to anticipate even the unlikely".

"I can't think you'll be troubled this evening: your young people seem such a friendly bunch".

"Oh, they are, most of the time".

"Your father told me that you were a teacher, but he didn't explain what subjects you taught. Are there many schools in England as small as yours? Or are there day-children as well?"

"No, we must be one of the smallest in the country with only fifteen boarding places".

We continued our meal in silence while Gordon digested the responses to his queries. Then he put down his knife and fork, took a sip of wine, placed his elbows on the table and clasped his hands together as a chinrest. His brow puckered, and he looked keenly into my eyes.

"How on earth do the parents manage to afford the fees? Your staffing ratio seems . . . very high".

"It's the one recommended by the Department of Education and Science for our type of school".

"Your . . . type . . . of . . . school", each word dropped out slowly and ruminatively. "and what type of school, if I may ask, *is* your school?"

"A Special School for Children under Stress, for girls with behavioural problems. Essentially a school to teach relationships".

Gordon's astonishment was comic. "Those girls I met this afternoon! But their behaviour seemed . . . charming: they were very well-mannered".

"That's why the D.E.S. in its wisdom, requires such a high staffing ratio. Our emphasis is on relationships: our aim is a harmonious familial atmosphere".

Gordon resumed his meal. 'Ah, I see; so the State pays for these children to attend your Special School. How does it decide which children shall be . . . sent?"

"Referred".

"Ah, *referred* to your type of school. Why will a girl be referred?"

"Usually there has been a breakdown of relationships. The parents — or parent — will have decided that she can no longer be coped with at home, or the girl herself may declare her . . . disaffection from her parents by herself taking the initiative, and absconding. Or there may be a problem at school, and the girl may truant, or, if the teachers take the initiative, she may be expelled".

The knife clanked on the side of Gordon's plate.

"Exp*ell*ed!" You mean those girls whom I met this evening have been expelled from school?"

"All except one of those you met".

"And the young woman who showed me round an hour or two ago was expelled from school, the one whom I took for a member of staff? They all had a good laugh when they realised my mistake".

"Stella is an unusually highly intelligent person, very articulate, and has a charming and friendly manner. She has been with us for several years and has become an accomplished guide and apologist for our ways. I'd prefer not to confirm whether she was expelled or not, but she'll be perfectly happy to tell you herself if you'd like to talk with her tomorrow".

"I'm sorry. I didn't mean to ask personal questions. I am just so astonished by those girls and by your school. In Australia we have schools for deaf children, for the blind, for slow-learners, and, of course, a different kind of institution altogether for juvenile delinquents. I've lost many a lad over the decades to such an establishment, but we have no school — as far as I know at any rate — for relationship problems".

"And I think that many English headteachers would not be aware of our type of school".

"How is it then that children are referred to your school?"

"I have some difficulty in answering that question. At one level, why **these** girls and not others in equal need and under similar stress, I simply don't know. I'm tempted to answer: an act of God. Not an all-seeing, all-directing God, I must add, but the One who acts in mysterious ways. To answer your question at another level, the simply practical, a teacher, through his or her headteacher, will bring the child to the attention of an educational psychologist, who may engage the help of a social worker. Then, after five years or so, when the child is at the end . . . **no**, when the child has **cut** his tether, the psychiatrist will call a Case Conference. You know the definition of a Case Conference, don't you? . . . No, no, of course not. As the Head of an ordinary School you will be innocent of such high-powered operations. So here it is: 'A case Conference is a convening of fellow-professionals who singly can do nothing for a child, but who together can decide that nothing can be done'.* And to someone else's aphorism, I add my own: 'A disturbed child shall be referred only when his problem has become irresoluble' ".

"That sounds rather cynical, Bryn".

Meg interposes: "You musn't take seriously all that Bryn says".

I am quite accustomed to artillery-fire behind my own lines from this quarter, and continue unabashed, "They are, I'm afraid, both truths, but happily not the whole truth. No, the odd headteacher or social worker, or educational psychologist, who cares for the individual child, will press for his or her welfare, and, eventually, the child will arrive at our school".

My speech had allowed Gordon to catch up on his main course, and now we all sit awaiting the dessert.

"That's very interesting because it's all very new to me, but let me turn to an area which is more familiar to me. How do you function as a **school**?"

"It's not really fair to other centres of academic excellence to class ours as a **school** . . . An **un**school, really. I am not using the word 'unschool' out of a wanton predilection for the paradox. When a child has suffered failure, for whatever reason, at school or home, we feel that we must offer her something different, perhaps radically different, from her arena of failure in the past. So we permit her to smoke under certain conditions. We do not insist on her attendance at class. We aim to enter into as egalitarian a relationship with her as possible. One of the means of achieving this is to hold an assembly each day which we call 'The Moot' ".

"The Moot? I visited a Moot-hall in Exeter when I was touring the West Country . . . "

"Yes. It's a very old word".

" . . . so I thought a 'Moot' was an ancient building. Yet you use it as if it meant 'school assembly' ".

---

* An even more extremely negative opinion of the Case Conference was expressed by a colleague who returned after a morning away from school, and exclaimed, "I'm never **ever** going to a Chaos Conference again". But he explained that it was only a Fraudian slip.

"I suppose a 'Moot' took place in a 'Moot-hall' or, in our case, a Mootoir, a 'Moot-room', and we **do** assemble".

"So what **is** a moot? How long does it last?"

"Its aim is a furtherance of the principle of egalitarianism. Its vehicle is that fine old English institution of Free Speech, as practiced at Hyde Park Corner, except that there is no need of a soap-box, as we sit in a circle so that each speaker may be seen by everyone else, and that heckling would be considered an impropriety. It usually lasts about an hour each day, but can go on for two, or even longer. Happy is the country with no History: happy is the community with a short Moot".

Gordon's spoon stopped short of its delve into the apple pie and custard. "One **hour**, you say . . . **two**. In Australia an assembly can last 10 minutes . . . fifteen if the playground is badly littered . . . but an **hour** . . . what do you talk about for an hour, pray?"

"Briefly, we discuss the stuff of relationships".

"Ah, you have a Course on Relationships?"

"Not exactly a Course. Someone with a different temperament to mine might have devised a syllabus covering all aspects of human relationships. My weakness is that I can't, or don't, plan. But a weakness is always the converse of a strength, as strength is of a weakness: like the forearms of a lame man, which became his thighs, to power his wheelchair. So the strength which my weakness in planning has engendered is a suppleness of response to the unexpected. Since the unexpected is the essence of emotional disturbance, it is an appropriate strength to cultivate".

The bowl of Gordon's spoon sinks slowly beneath the custard. He seems more disoriented on familiar than he had been on alien territory.

"Does every school in England begin the day with a Moot?"

"Oh no. On a recent straw-count, conducted by **The Guardian**, there were only about half a dozen in the country".

"How do you evaluate the effectiveness of this mode of instruction?"

"I don't know that anyone's considered it worthy of scholarly evaluation. An educational psychologist once visited our school, attended one Moot, and remarked on his departure that it was 'the most participative group discussion' he had encountered. He subsequently wrote a book about our type of school, having visited many of them, so perhaps his opinion is as authoritative as any. He didn't, however, refer us any children, so perhaps he didn't rate participativeness in itself too highly. For my own part, I value it deeply: at its lowest it is communication, establishing a currency of thought among members of a large family; at its highest it is a form of communion amongst us. I have not evaluated it formally; for me its worth is a matter of blind faith".

"I see, but how do you prepare for the Moot?"

"We prepare ourselves with a short silence, letting our minds go empty — if we can — and then we just plunge in, raising points for communal discussion".

"Ah, points for discussion. This has been the girls' homework, I take it".

"No. It is purely spontaneous on their part, although we do encourage each one to recognise her contribution to events and to assume responsibility for communal harmony. I did say that a preparedness for the unexpected was a useful frame of mind to cultivate".

"And how do you get them to start, to use their own initiative?"

"The problem is how to get them — or rather us — to stop".

"You say you can go talking together for over an hour?"

"Yes".

"How on earth do you sustain their interest for such a long period? How do you motivate them?"

"I suppose we're prepared to listen. Each new girl sits and stares for a period, but she soon gets the hang of it".

"Well, Bryn and Meg, I think you're being too modest. I do admire your both investing yourselves so comprehensively in stimulating your girls to talk about themselves and to accept responsibility for their misbehaviour. Anyway, I look forward to attending my first Moot to-morrow morning, when perhaps I may begin to understand what it's all about. Now tell me about the rest of the school day, please. What follows the Moot?"

"A break, then Class-time".

"**Ah**!" exclaimed Gordon, followed by a long silence, while he looked from one to the other of us, smiling, his long-furrowed brow now cleared. "**Now** I understand the motivation of the Moot. It stands clear to me now. Your children are talking so long in order to delay going to work in class", and he fell to his apple pie with zest.

A Belittling Life

"You musn't take it to heart, Bryn: we work in The Failure Industry. You have served Lyn well over the past two years. We were on the point of having to borstalise her when we heard about your school. You and your staff and the school as a community gave her some happiness and security during two years respite from a deprived and at times depraved home background. If only that father hadn't skipped the nest as we closed in, we would have had him sent away for a 10-stretch for the way he treated Lyn during her teenage".

"Thanks, Steve, for trying to reassure me, and thanks for calling in to tell me what happened to Lyn. But **prison** — within 6 months of leaving school . . . and the youngest member of the Security Wing by two years . . .

A knock at the door. "Come in, Carol. You remember Steve don't you?"

"Yeh, It's Lyn's Probation Officer, in' it? Hi, Steve. 'Ow's Lyn? . . .

". . . Is she? I told 'er she was stoopid to leave just becoz she'd reached 'er sixteenf birfday. Anyway, Bryn. When we goin' on this outing? You said 'Be ready for 10' an' it's aff past nah. The girls is all waitin' in the van".

"I'm sorry, Carol. Steve called unexpectedly just to tell us about Lyn as he was passing through . . ."

"And I must be on my way again, Bryn. It's been grand talking with you again. Thank Meg for all those cups of coffee. Ah well, back to the Failure Industry . . . "

Numbly working my professional treadmill, I clambered into the motor caravan which acts as mobile classroom and excursion coach during term-time, and my own Unravelhome during the holidays, and started the ignition.

Where were we going today? I had thought to go to Alton Towers, that universally signposted Mecca of the pleasure-seeker, but my mood ill-disposed me to respond to the merry-making and raucousness of my little group of girls. I thought of the outings when Lyn had accompanied us with her own share of raucousness . . . Of the time when she thoughtlessly used most of the bread to feed the ducks, and we all came home hungry . . . Of the time when that stray dog came running up to her, and she insisted on taking it to a Police Station before we could go on our planned outing to the Ice Rink. And then how we had picked up a wandering police constable to take us to his station to deposit the animal in the kennels . . . No, I can't go to Alton Towers. The Failure Industry, eh? A good phrase. 'A belittling life, my brethren'.

"Excuse me, Bryn". Tim's gentle voice from the back of the van. I usually take him out with us, and drop him like a pigeon about 10 miles out for him to run back to school. "Did you say you were going to . . . ?" He paused, because he knows that I never tell the girls where we are going on our outings.

"No, I've changed my mind, Tim. I'm going somewhere else. I'll take you all the way".

"But, Bryn, I don't want to go too far".

"Trust me this time, brother. I've somewhere special in mind — for you and me anyway".

Tim's gasp of admiration as we crested the panorama-point of Monsal Head was reward enough, and, clad in running strip, he clambered out eagerly.

"I know it's 25 miles from home, Tim, but you can run round the tops and rejoin us in an hour in the dale and I can take you back nearer to school".

Before I was in second gear he was out of earshot and we saw only his black locks bobbing as he descended the valley.

We lunched pleasantly enough, Rose taking over the spreading of the sandwiches, while I acted as drinks-waiter.

Lunch over, I do the washing-up and wait for someone to realise the grandeur of our situation and express a desire to go and explore the woods and the stream purling just outside the door of the van.

"Can we 'ave our fag in the van, Bryn. There's nowhere to sit out there".

A belittling life.

"No: Bryn won't let us smoke in 'ere. It's no use askin'. Can we 'ave the rest of the bread to feed the ducks, Bryn?"

So they are induced out of the little enclave of civilisation into the glorious wilderness which surrounds us. I distribute white nicotine wafers and feel like a priest forced to conduct some form of satanic communion in his Cathedral. A belittling life, indeed.

And here's one of them coming back to annoy me.

"You can't come in here now, Dawn. Only one can stand up in the van at a time and I'm here doing the washing-up".

"Yes, Bryn, but" . . . twirling her unlit cigarette between listless fingers, "I don't know whether to 'ave me fag or not".

"That's up to you". And, irritably, "It was only on Monday that you brought a note from your dad authorising you to have 5 fags a day after we have done our utmost to restrict you to 2. The lighter's over there".

"No, what I mean is that I don't know whether to give up smoking altogether. When I was at me Karate lesson last night, Toni — that's me teacher — told me it was bad for me 'ealth".

I exploded. "But Dawn, we've been telling you that for twelve months. We've got posters all over the school, and booklets and leaflets everywhere". (Did I mind, I wonder, that the word of a 19-year-old girl with an acquaintance of a few weeks has had more effect than my year-long therapeutic relationship with Dawn?)

"Anyway", recovering myself, "The packet is over there. My hands are wet. Put your cigarette back if you're really determined to give up".

The others are crowding back now, and I haven't had a moment to myself this lunch-time.

"When we goin', Bryn?"

"But we haven't been here more than half an hour while we've lunched. What about exploring round here? Do you see that bridge over there. You can cross it and there's a path on to an old railway track which leads to a viaduct from which you can see . . . "

"No thanks, Bryn. It's boring 'ere. Can't we go?"

(Adolescent girls! Give me Primary-age kids, who'd have been

113

scrambling up the screes, climbing the trees, and getting soaking wet in the Wye. But all I said, my mind well professionally calloused, was)

"No, we've got to wait in case Tim comes back. I'm just going out to explore. You come too".

But such blandishments fall on deaf ears, and I stride off, stick twirling, spirits rising.

A padding of feet makes me turn round.

"Can I come?" Much as I relish my own company, I enjoy the company of a child . . . only just less . . . and even more if she can savour her surroundings.

"Of course, Dawn".

We strolled arm-in-arm in companionate silence, stood looking at the flowing water from the bridge, and walked hand-in-hand along the track towards the viaduct.

Dawn stopped by the board describing the history of the Trail and the fauna, and picked out the words she recognised on it. She had been severely educationally disadvantaged throughout her school-life before she had been expelled a couple of years ago for intolerable violence of behaviour, and now, aged 15, could not read enough of the words to make any kind of sense of the notice. This may have been the first academic task she had undertaken of her own initiative, and, unconstrained by the walls of the classroom and an audience of potentially jeering classmates, she rigorously set herself to decipher the hitherto impenetrable script.

"No, don't tell me the **whole** word, Bryn. I just meant **this** bit of it".

And so, totally absorbed, she picked her way painstakingly along the track of comprehension, using me as a guide when needed: I did not lead from in front, but pointed out the way from behind.

Dawn's face glowed as we made our way back to base, and expressed pleasure at her achievement and talked of her aspirations.

"I now see that you are serious in your desire to stop smoking, Dawn. May I advise you not to tell the others? This bunch will only try to get you to start again. Just jealousy, really. They'd like to stop themselves, but since they can't, they'll do their utmost to prevent anyone else's achieving it. Pretend you've got a bad throat. Tell 'em you'd like to smoke, but the discomfort . . . the pain . . . And you can't bear to be in the same room as anyone smoking because of the temptation . . . you understand me? We've tried to help so many girls give up smoking over the years that I realise how difficult it is. We're nearly back at the van now, so not a word about 'giving up' . . . O.K. . . . Hi, girls, hasn't Tim turned up yet? We can't wait much longer. He said he'd run all the way, but surely he can't run what is virtually a Marathon and still be on duty at 4 o'clock . . . ?"

"Wouldn't put it past him. You know Tim".

"We'll perhaps pick him up on the road back".

Pity really. I had hoped to introduce Tim to the august medievalism of

Haddon Hall this afternoon. Ah well, we've got to go . . .

Arrived at our destination, we debouch at the car park and I issue the usual instructions for the comfort and protection of other visitors, and advice on how to make the most of one's time at a Museum. Walk: don't run. Whisper: don't talk. Sip: don't gulp. It's not a race . . .

. . . But most are in and out of the first room before I have passed the entrance doorway. What's the bloody use?

. . . But Dawn's eye is caught by some detail, and she turns to ask me a question.

I feel torn between my supervisory responsibility towards the others who are already out of earshot and my educational responsibility towards Dawn, who saunters from room to room gazing curiously, occasionally asking a question.

I settle for my higher duty and we do not encounter the others until we reach the trinkets in the Gift Shop.

Rose sidles up to me casually, pretends to examine a poster, and speaks to me in an undertone out of the corner of her mouth.

"You know that new girl, Bryn? What's her name . . .? Yes, that's right: Clare. You'll 'ave to keep an eye on 'er, Bryn. She pinched a pair of earrings on a card. She waited till she thought we wasn't looking, then nudged them . . . accidentally-on-purpose like, off the shelf on to her shoe so's it wouldn't make a noise as it hit the floor. Then wiped 'er nose and dropped 'er 'anky. I'd come up be'ind 'er by then and said, 'Them ear-rings come off that shelf there', just as if I didn't know she was going to pinch 'em. I didn't want the school to get in no trouble 'cause of 'er".

"Thanks, Rose. You've done a good job there".

" 'S all right, Bryn. Soon as I saw 'er on Monday I **noo** she was a tea-leaf. "An", with grudging admiration, "she's nifty".

"We'd better get back to the van".

"Righto". And, as if she thought I were too other-worldly. "I'll go an' keep an eye on 'er meself". She moved away from me casually.

I stood numbly on the spot where Rose had left me, my mind trying to balance an irrational disgust with this act of theft with my warmth at Rose's loyalty to the school. My eyes focused on the poster which Rose had pretended to read:

A Modern Version of the 23rd Psalm
The Lord is my Pace-setter — I shall not rush.
He makes me stop for quiet intervals.
He provides me with images of stillness which restore my serenity.
He leads me in ways of efficiency through calmness of mind,
And his guidance is peace . . .

I felt a tug at my elbow. It was Dawn. We walked together down from the Courtyard, the others already in the distance. She began to demonstrate to me Karate exercises. I responded in conventional politeness about a subject which held little interest for me. Then her movements arrested my attention. She straight-punched the air, she side-kicked from a perfect balance, with energy and discipline. There was more to this Martial Arts business than I would have admitted to. It wasn't just mugging people in a scientific way, as I had, in my ignorance, supposed.

"Do that again".

"Which one".

But at that moment a shout from ahead distracted us.

"Come on, Bryn". Rose was calling, and I noticed that several of the others were pointing at Dawn and jeering.

I waved reassuringly.

"Now can I suggest to you, Dawn, that not only do you not tell the others that you intend to stop smoking but that you don't do your Karate exercises in public. There's a certain type of person who . . . Well, just take my word for it. Now, why not combine the two new patterns of behaviour . . . to re-inforce each other. Each fag-time go to your room and practice your exercises solitarily. I'm most impressed by your discipline and how much you've learnt in such a short time . . .

"Yes, yes. Here are the keys, Clare. Now let's look out for Tim as we make our way back to school. Poor lad: he must be exhausted.

But I need not have worried. As we arrived, hot steam was issuing from the bathroom, and Tim stood radiantly smiling and rubbing his hair with a towel.

In the privacy of his room, I recounted our day.

"The new girls we have this term are hard nuts, but Dawn is a brand we may yet snatch from the blaze, if we're vigilant. She has decided to give up smoking. Now you know that I have grown cynical over the years about that kind of aspiration, but let's try and support her . . . I've advised her to . . . (I might have had more confidence in Dawn — and in human nature — on that day had I the foreknowledge that the cigarette which Dawn fingered in Monsal Dale was to be the last that she would touch while at our school. The next time she was tempted was the day, 8 months later, the week after passing her Orange Belt, when she sat her C.S.E. English exam, and she nervously fingered a cigarette. As on that previous occasion, she forebore — and passed the exam creditably).

"And what sort of day did you have, Tim".

"Oh, Bryn, I am most grateful to you for introducing me to Monsal Dale. It is a most wonderful place, and I've had one of the best day's running I've

116

had for years. As I was coming through the fields near Cromford, I had a 'runner's high'. Is that a term familiar to you? No, well it's a kind of exaltation, a peak-experience, that comes to a runner only once in many a hundred mile . . . "

So I went off duty from the Failure Industry feeling that it's perhaps not such a belittling life, after all.

An Opportunity for Counselling

We are rambling along in the Unravelhome after a sun-soaked afternoon at the Stables, walking the dogs, talking with Ann in her kitchen, blushing at her 25-year-old son Tom working on the engine of his car, seeing the world from a perspective twice as high, astride a living, moving platform, with Sally safely holding the reins.

Lorna has prevented my dictating any letters, as I customarily do on Thursday afternoons, by her desultry talk as she sits next to me, telling me about her mates back home, what they did on Saturday afternoons . . . school . . . a hundred lines . . . Standing under the clock outside the Headmaster's room . . . The Police . . . the evasions . . . and she hadn't even been there when it happened . . . "

She is now talking about her family, and I begin to have a very clear impression of the inter-relationship of the three girls and two boys, of their jockeying for attention and position in the race-course of their 3-bedroomed Council house under the wayward stewardship of her mother and father.

I have listened to many a thousand hours of such chatter, and half-tuned out of listening so that another waveband of my mind could address itself to devising some strategy for intervening in the damaging familial strife. Could I invite the social worker to visit? How much of what Lorna was telling me, in the cosy confidentiality of sitting next to me, would she allow me to transmit? Was the social worker whom I'd met briefly a year ago, sensitive enough to . . .

My antenna senses a sudden change and strength of signal and I turn to find Lorna's eyes intently on me as she tells me about herself. Did I know that her real Dad had left the home when she was only one year old? Did I think it was **her** fault that her Dad had gone? It isn't difficult to reassure her, in words at least, on this point. But there is something else troubling her, I know. Had I met her other brothers and sisters? Did I know that she was the eldest? that her father was her stepfather?

Another glance at her troubled face tells me that these matters were of deep significance to her. I have to keep facing the front to pay attention to the traffic. Has she, I wonder, chosen this situation so that she can avoid a literally face-to-face conversation?

But no, she has not chosen this moment. She **has** to tell me, she has to unlock this coffin in the dark crypt of her mind.

"Actually, Bryn, me Mum and me real Dad didn't know each other very long at all. As a matter of fact . . . " Her words are casual in intent, but her bitten-nailed fingers twirl a ringlet till it is so tight that she has to reverse-roll to release it. "An' when I said that 'e left 'ome, it weren't quite right, 'coz they never **act**ually 'ad a 'ome to leave. Me Mum lived with 'er mum an' dad all the time they knew each other . . . "

She wants me to draw inferences to save **her** having to utter the painful truth. I hesitate, fearful at compounding the hurt by the wrong words.

"So you see, Bryn", irritably at my non-response, "me Mum and me real Dad wasn't married an' . . . an' . . . I . . . " Outside, the traffic lights turn red and I halt the vehicle.

I look into her face, and know that this time she can't continue. For her this is the ultimate pain. The moment has arrived when the deep of my psychological insight into the disturbed child-mind, distilled over 20 years, shall call unto the deep of her emotional agony.

I stare ahead. The lights change to red-and-amber. I take one last long look into her eyes before I engage the clutch. My instinct tells me the words I want to use, but my mental computer is flashing red at me furiously.

I press the accelerator in response to the green light, as I utter the words: "Well, I always thought you were a right little bastard, but I didn't know you really are one".

I ease into third gear before I dare look to find out whether my instinct or my mental computer were right. I perceive that her body quivers, her head is bent, her white-knuckled fingers grip her knees, and when she rocks back I see her face flushed and tears in her eyes.

. . . Tears of laughter. Helpless laughter. Then she collects herself.

"I've never told anyone about me bein' a bastard before, an' I didn't fink you'd joke about it . . . "

A Rare Branch of the Martial Arts leads to a Pacific Act of Disarming

Wyn had been trying to retire for years.

At about the usual age she had retired from the Probation Service and come North to live with her daughter and family. Still wondrously vigorous, she found that the activities of the local Women's Institute didn't absorb her abundant energy, and she looked around for a little part-time work. She saw an advertisement for a school secretary, and her letter joined 30 or so others on my clip-file. In the course of time she was short-listed and appointed to perform the multifarious duties of the Bursar/Secretary of the new school. A year later, at our first anniversary/survival celebrations, she disclosed to us that while she was awaiting us in the Office, her eye had been caught by a pencilled note on the calendar by the time of **her** interview: "The nice lady", though how Meg could have intuited this opinion from a typewritten letter I do not know. I always said that we appointed our first cook as soon as she walked through the front door from her face, and our first secretary from her type-face.

Five years after her first unsuccessful attempt at retirement, during which Wyn had become plenipotentiary in all matters administrative, Mother Confessor, and dear friend, she suddenly gave in her notice — to take effect any time over the following 12 months when we had appointed someone else. And a year after the expiry of **that** time, or two years after her 'notice', when Marian had joined us as a worthy successor, and seven years after Wyn's original 'retirement', here she is again listening to the story of our latest difficulties.

"I know you had to cut back on staff when the numbers on roll dropped, but you'll have to find someone else after this latest influx of admissions . . . If I can help in any way . . . What about Typing? I always wanted to be a teacher . . . but in those days, when I was a girl, such ambitions were not easy to fulfil . . . "

We readily assented, and saw her hands clasp each other and eyes glisten eagerly, as a student's might when offered her first post, or a young teacher's in her prime her first headship.

Then the expression on her face became grave.

"But I hope I'll suit you in this different capacity, Bryn. I have the greatest respect for your . . . latitude in academic matters but", she paused, and raised both eyes aloft in supplication for heavenly forgiveness, "I'm of the Old School, I'm afraid. Never could stop working myself, and I expect it of others. I'm quite happy for the girls to have the option of coming to Typing classes, but if they **do** choose to come, I shall work them hard. I know you are all for **zest** in learning, but **I** see the value of academic **rigour**". Her hand became a fist and with a circular action pestled the idea to a fine powder. "I believe that people become happy by their own initiative and effort. Once you set your hand to the plough, you should follow it". She extended her hands in self-deprecation. "Sorry. You can't teach old dogs new tricks. Are you sure you want me in your school?"

"Our dear Wyn, we have got to know your bad qualities as well as your good over this past 7 years, and they are, in an Heraclitean way, the same. You've tolerated my . . . ah, latitude, in all sorts of ways; don't you think that I could extend the same liberality to a young teacher on the threshold of her new career. Welcome to the teaching staff of Rowen House!"

"Bryn!", Wyn's shoulders shook, "what day shall I start?"

The new teacher arrived on a beautiful summer September afternoon in the glorious Autumn of 1986. She seemed, however, uncharacteristically unprepared to take off her coat and start work. She clasped her handbag in front of her, and spoke to her new headteacher as if on a point of high principle.

"Had you noticed, Bryn, that the sun is shining outside?"

"I had, as a matter of fact".

"And did you know that we are in the height of the blackberry season?"

"Not really".

"Ah", and her tone softened, as if that excused me. "Well, it's a bumper crop this year and I think that it could do the girls a world of good to get some fresh air and go and pick some".

"What about your Typing?"

"It's a question of priorities, Bryn. We shan't get many more lovely days like this after an awful Summer. Now if you think it's more important to teach Typing on a day like this", and she shrugged her shoulders and pursed her lips, as before an impregnable educational Mr. Bumble, "then of course I shall reluctantly comply with your wishes".

"I take your point, of course, but I think we ought to put your proposal to the vote in a Moot".

"Oh dear: those Moots **do** drag on so. It's a question of priorities. Anyway, I'll wait for you in my room".

"I see it as a question of the propriety of an individual taking decisions in a democratic community with group consultation. And I think you ought to attend the Moot to put your own case".

"If you wish".

"Let's get started then, girls. Firstly, I want to inform you about a new option the school is offering. Several of you are still here who went to Adam's Karate classes last year. And you remember that last term Mike came once a week and offered Tai Chi, which is a kind of dance of the whole body aiming at gracefulness of movement? Well, this term Wyn is coming in on Mondays to offer another branch of the Martial Arts, which is called Ty Ping, which is a dance of the fingers, aiming at strength and lissomness. Now I know that several of you were keen to start learning the movements of Ty Ping, but I may have to disappoint you. You see, Wyn has made the highly irresponsible proposal that we should go out this afternoon to pick blackberries instead of staying in and learning a skill which will be useful to you throughout your lives".

Wyn: "I really don't know why Bryn is going on about it. We've got all Winter to learn Typing, and we probably shan't get another day like this all year".

Neil: "Perhaps I can explain Bryn's lack of comprehension, Wyn. You know that he is interested in several European languages, in which he is accustomed to translate directly and simply from one language to another, word for word. What he can't understand is the subtlety of the Oriental tongues, in which the inflexion of the voice in differing circumstances can mean different things. For instance, **Ty** Ping, stressed in the first syllable in the winter means 'The Art of Finger-Dance': but Ty **Ping** stressed in the second, and in the Autumn, means 'Blackberry Picking'. Now who votes for **Ty** Ping this afternoon? One. And who votes for Ty **Ping**? Carried overwhelmingly. Hard luck, Bryn. The Blacks have it. Anyone for berries?"

Wyn leads the way to her newly-discovered haven for blackberry picking, a real beauty spot. Across a newly-mown wheat-field, I stride out to keep up with her. "I can see the zest for this outing, Wyn, but what happened to 'academic rigour'?"

"This is the stuff of education, Bryn. The collection of wild fruits, its cleaning and preparation for to-morrow's luncheon. Come on, girls", as we breast the summit of a small hill. "we've plenty of work to do". I fall back now, the more leisurely to admire the panorama of Derbyshire farming hillscape which lies before me.

"Look at the vista, girls", comes the new teacher's voice from the declivity, barely audible to her struggling, panting charges behind her.

I give Julie my basket, so I might have reason to continually approach her in a non-threatening way. She has been at the school only four days, and is distinctly apprehensive about my person and presence, calling me 'sir', or rather 'suh', on the few occasions she had managed to respond to my friendly overtures to her, and doing a circuit of the room once, round two tables, to pick up a plate which had been just out of her reach by me at the outset.

I deposit my first handful of berries and remark, staring hard at the horizon so that she can study me without interruption.

"I'm sorry if you feel dumped in a new school away from home, Julie. We will do our best to make you feel at ease and happy here. The girls seem to like you even though you don't say very much. Ah well, better get on with my job of picking".

I bring a second handful. "I realise that you are a bit wary of me, Julie, which is why I haven't spoken to you much this week, but it doesn't mean that I don't care about you. If you don't want to talk to me, I won't take it personally; just ask one of the other girls to tell me what you want . . . Oh, look, there's a big bunch up there. It's out of your reach, I think . . . "

After my third: "I want you to know that we are prepared to go out of our way to accommodate you here, to help you to be happy. And if, after a reasonable period, you decide you can't settle here, then I won't keep you, and you can try your luck elsewhere".

So far I had said nothing which required a response: now I essayed a remark which could be construed as a question.

"I'd like to get to know you better, and I wonder whether Meg and I might come and visit you at home — when you feel like inviting us, of course".

"'S all roi' boi me", the thick Brummy brogue responded.

"Thanks", and I walked off at the behest of the teacher, who was calling a halt to her Ty Ping class for the day.

I am mounting the stubble-field alone when I hear the rustle of dry stalks behind me. To my surprise it is Julie, and we walk together in awkward silence for 50 yards or so.

"'Ave you iver bin stopped boi the P'lice for possessing offensive weapons?"

It is a novel opening to a conversation, for which my past experience has not furnished me with a ready response.

I look into the horizon, glance momentarily into a face which is studying mine most carefully, resume my long gaze, and then reply.

"Can't say I have, really", as if possessing offensive weapons hadn't been one of the many reasons why I had been stopped by the Police — not that I could remember, at least. I look down to find that her eyes are now intent on my horizon, and an ugly, rusty jack-knife lies in her hand.

"I guess you feel you need that knife to protect yourself, Julie, but . . . I wonder if you'd mind asking in the Moot if you could keep it while you're at school.

"'S'all roi': you 'ave it".

A Wild-Gril Chase

Our family of four stood on the edge of the footpath on a busy road in a neighbouring city waiting for the traffic to clear in order to cross. My teenage son was going for an appointment at the orthodontist's which might last anything up to an hour.

"I think I'll just pop into the secondhand bookshops while we're waiting", with an airy wave behind me up the road.

"We haven't any more room for books at home" rejoined Meg, "and besides we can't afford the money at the moment until we get some more girls referred. Why can't you spend the time thinking how we can do that . . . . Look", pointing across the road with outstretched arm at the answer to her prayer, "look, Social Services Department . . . just across there. Go and ask them if they have any disturbed girls they want referring. That'll be a really **use**ful way of spending the hour".

"But you know perfectly well that we have approached this Local Authority in the past without success . . . . " A gap appeared in the traffic, and I was left mouthing alone on the edge of the pavement. I continued the argument, however, silently, and recalled how I had written to, then visited, the Central Education Office five years before, how I had written to each regional Education Office 3 years ago, how I had written to the Central and All the Regional Social Service Departments only 12 months ago, and we had had no flicker of a response to any of these overtures. Such a visit now could only be a complete waste of effort.

Having thus fortified my mind with such incontrovertible reasoning, in the face of Meg's unreason, I walked across the road, through the portals of the Social Services Department and found myself standing before the glass grille where the receptionist looked up courteously at my approach.

With the contrary reasoning to my being there so strongly and so recently in my mind, I expressed myself only diffidently.

"I am the headmaster of a small school for disturbed adolescent girls, and I wondered whether your department wishes to place any such children?"

I had time to weigh myself in the mirror of the receptionist's eyes: I didn't **dress** like a headmaster; I didn't **look** like a headmaster, as I stood nervously passing my hands over my body trying to find the wallet which might accredit my preposterous claim; and, indeed, I no longer **felt** like a headmaster. I continued to look into the receptionist's eyes, as she appraised me, and I felt like a dirty old man with a dubious, if novel, line in procuring the company of teenage girls. Behind me I heard the low keening of a child. A young female growl followed, then a sharp smack, and a prolonged shrilling.

"I beg your pardon . . . I didn't hear what you . . . the baby".

"I said that we don't get much call for . . . that . . . here". Then, helpfully, as if she did not wish to seem wanting in courtesy, or, cynically, as if she wanted to carry on with the real work of her day, "but did you know that there is another Social Services Office a few doors higher up and, yet another about a hundred yards further on still?"

I stood on the edge of the kerb of this street of a thousand secondhand bookshops, beguiling me across there, and a thousand Social Services Departments like a ball & chain over here. The traffic did not relent, and I strolled up the road . . . and found myself outside the second Social Services Department. Just one more try, just so that I can tell Meg . . .

I joined a small queue this time, which gave me a chance to collect myself and compose a more plausible, or less implausible, approach — and observe my fellow-clients. Old people of both sexes sat about in postures of numb composure. Several young women, each with children, one accompanied by her mother, but none by a husband. From the low hubbub surfaced key words, strongly expressed, as "the rent", "me claim", "overdue".

My turn. I began, only slightly discomposed by the sudden thought that her colleague down the road might have warned this one about my visit.

"I-wrote-to-the-Head-of-the-Social-Services-Department-at-this-Office-several-weeks-ago-to-appraise-him-of-the-existence-of-our-newly-opened-school-for-behaviourally-disordered-or-maladjusted-youngsters,-and-I-just-popped-in-to-ask-whether-it-might-be-profitable-to-have-a-chat-with-his-or-her-representative?"

Ponderously matey, quaintly erudite: in a word, headmasterly.

"Pardon".

. . . but perhaps too polished. Take it a bit slower this time.

"I wrote to the Director of the Social Services . . . " and I became aware of a young man, who had crossed the office behind her and dropped some papers into the receptionist's tray . . . "to have a chat with his or her representative".

"Ah, I'm afraid that we don't have much call . . . "

"It's all right, Glenys. I'll take this one", the young man interposed. "If you'd like to take a seat in the waiting-room across the foyer, Mr. er . . . I'll be with you in a moment".

It was, as moments in waiting rooms go, quite short, but long enough for me to wonder whether the young man had not come out of the inner office in response to that telephone call from the receptionist down the road, and was even now collecting a couple of 'heavies' to come and interview me. If only I had gone where *I* wanted to this morning. Why did Meg send me on these wild-girl chases?

. . . When the young man walked in, introduced himself as Godfrey, and sat down companionably and informally, with a clip-board.

"Now, Bryn, let's hear something about your school . . . Why have we never heard anything about it before? . . . You did? . . . Well, it never came my way".

And so, however I may have dressed that day, and however I may have looked, I began to *feel* like a Headmaster again, as I discoursed, professional to professional, with Godfrey for over an hour.

I walked out happy. I would have felt even more self-satisfied if I could have known that 18 months later our school roll would have 50% of Godfrey-induced referrals.

I stroll care-free down my side of the road towards the orthodontist's, when I am arrested by a call from the other.

Meg and the two children join me, and she gets in the first word.

"Where on earth have you **been**? You said that you were going to the second-hand bookshops. We've been trailing up and down this road in and out of **every** one. We're **starv**ing. Oh, Bryn . . . why can't you keep to arrangements? Why can't you **ever** do **any**thing right?"

Julia's nine-year-old voice pipes up, "That's what Olly says to Stan".

Woman in Camera

"What I want to know is, Where's Meg?"

"She's at home, Wyn. I've come to see you on my bike".

I was delivering my latest tousle of handwriting for Wyn to unravel and knit into her neat rows of typescript.

"No, no. I mean that I have typed upwards of 50 of these episodes of yours over the past year or so, and not one represents Meg in the vitally important role which, I'm sure you'll agree, she plays in the school".

"Oh, I see what you mean. It's funny you should put the question in that way. It's how I'm greeted any morning when she doesn't happen to arrive at school at the same time as me: 'Where's Meg?' Not 'Hello Bryn' but 'Where's Meg?' And I remember some years ago, Carole came into the Moot Room a bit late one morning with that gleaming Carribean smile of hers. Then she stopped short, almost panic-stricken, and said 'Where's Meg?' It is as if Carole intuited that Meg wasn't in the building that morning. And it's the same throughout any ordinary school-day. Every hour. 'Where's Meg?' 'Where's Meg?' Woman much missed, how they call for you".

"Yes, I can understand that, Bryn. But that doesn't answer my question".

And of course Wyn is right: the weft of these stories would not hold together without the woof of Meg's presence in the school. She is the community's mother-figure — in meaningful etymon, its matrix. She is not merely the headteacher's wife, the little woman behind the Man with the Camera. No, she has a camera of her own: a **camera interna**, a private room, in which whereof we cannot speak, thereof we must pass over in silence. And, of course, what we pass over in silence cannot be written down. I make no excuse for the fact that by far the most interesting, intimate, and most instructive aspects of the school may not be described in these pages, for reasons of confidentiality. If you would know the merely constabulary foot-work of our daily life, follow me through these pages: if you would understand the psychological detective work, the confrontation with Reality, the dramatic confession, the emotional melting pot, you must be a fly on the wall of Meg's **camera interna**: I am Inspector Lestrade to her Sherlock Holmes.

I cannot reveal the matter, but I can essay a description of the manner of Meg's counselling technique.

On one occasion, in the early years, before I realised the importance of total privacy to confidentiality, I entered Meg's sanctum and became immediately aware of the quality of stillness in the air. A deeply sensitive and highly intelligent teenage girl sat head-hung, her long blonde hair valencing her face. Kim was perfectly articulate in normal social situations, charming, with a warm manner which made her particularly good with young children. However, there were occasions when personal stresses occluded her usual self, and once she actually dissembled a mute successfully with strangers for a considerable length of time.

Now, on the occasion I recount, she sits unspeaking and quite still. Meg talks discursively, as if she had no goal, so softly as to be heard only by the inner ear, by Kim's troubled inner self. She talks about her mother, to whom Kim is deeply attached, about her father, who is a dismembered limb from the family whose stump still bleeds, and about each of her siblings.

Meg is running her verbal palms over the surface of Kim's life, as a skilful masseuse will palpate the muscles, until she finds the painful knot, and her experienced fingers knead it gently and firmly. Kim's response is but a tremor of the valance, which intimates that Meg has located the hidden wound.

Subsequently, after many hours of near silence with Kim over the weeks and months, a dialogue began, developed, and, eventually for a season, reached flood proportions.

And so, over the years of our colleagueship, I become accustomed to one troubled child after many a hundred other go seeking about the premises. "Where's Meg?" "Do you know where Meg is?" "Ah, **there** you are; can I have a word with you? . . . No, a **private** word, please".

)

There is another aspect to Meg's influence in the school, as attested by an observation of Tim's.

Emotionally wrung by the latest passage-at-arms with one of the girls, we three sit silently sipping coffee. They are all asleep now, one with dry tear-furrows down her cheeks, her hair stroked smooth by a woman's gentle hand.

Tim stares hard into the gas fire, smiling contently as one who reviews a hard job well completed, and addresses the hissing jets. "You know, the . . . the exhilarating thing about working with Bryn . . . "

During his long pause, for Tim was never one to rush to explain himself simply when the mot juste would do, I assume a facial expression of becomingly modest abstraction, and prepare to simper my disclaimers . . . until I realise that this master of the diplomatic reproof was about to serve me with one. "The exhilarating thing about working at Rowen House is that Bryn is a risk-taker".

Through the uncurtained window the clouds scud past the full moon, while we three deliberate upon the appropriateness of Tim's word. I nod my head indeterminately, as if I didn't know whether to bow to the accolade or side-step the sword thrust.

Meg takes another sip of coffee. "I know what you mean, Tim, but Corinne has been boiling up now for several weeks and it needed . . .

lancing".

"Oh, yes, Meg. I do agree. I **did** say that I find it exhilarating to work with Bryn when he is, to use his phrase, "playing swashbuckle", when he is the risk-taker, but I also find it immensely reassuring to have Meg's balming presence as the . . . the . . . risk-**curber** in the background".

While I have outlined Meg's two main functions, as Counsellor and Risk-curber, it must not be thought that she operates only in an Ivory Tower of the mind. She is also practical, able to deal with the most basic, indeed fundament-al, bodily movements, as the following episode illustrates: not so much Woman **in camera**, as Woman **in cloaco**.

A decade or two ago our marital relationship extended itself into full-time colleagueship when we opened a day-school for emotionally disturbed children in Lancashire, under the auspices of the Local Educational Authority.

One day, when we were well-established, a social worker had made an arrangement to bring a mother and child to visit the school. They familiarised themselves with the premises under Meg's guidance, while the Social Worker essayed a description to me of the problem which 6-year-old Victor was presenting at home and school. It appeared that Victor was a dear, merry, affectionate, intelligent little boy, and that his mother was responsible and caring. She had already successfully brought up older members of her family into young adulthood.

"That sounds fine. As you know, I am strongly in favour of referring the child as young as possible, as this is economical of our professional time, and, more importantly, preventive of child distress. Hitherto your Child Guidance Clinic has not seemed disposed to . . . implement the principle. What on earth has Victor **done** to be brought to our attention so young?"

"Oh, he hasn't **done** anything. As I say, he's a charming little boy. He reads well, which I understand that few of even your older children do when they reach you, and he works well in the classroom".

"That sounds good, but . . . "

"But he does have one li-tt-le problem".

"Ah . . . "

"Yes, he's encopretic".

"I see. I've dealt with children in residential school who soil, of course, but we're a day school. Would Victor not be more appropriately placed in some kind of boarding establishment?"

"The poor mother is at her wit's end to know **what** to do, and, of course, Victor is becoming very anxious, especially as the mother/child relationship is **bas**ically a very close and loving one".

" . . . a boarding establishment like the psychiatric hospital in the town".

"Yes, but we didn't want to distance mother-and-child".

"In terms of **distance**, the hospital is closer to their home — they live

127

on Heath Road, didn't you say — than our school is".

"That's true. In fact, to be perfectly frank with you, we did refer Victor to the Hospital School **first** . . . : but the problem there is . . . that . . . well, to put it into a few words, is . . . that the Child Psychiatrist doesn't feel it's . . . well . . . appropriate to treat Victor on his ward".

"In a word — knowing the Child Psychiatrist as we both do — he doesn't **want** to".

"In a word . . . No".

"Hmm. Of course, how the Child Psychiatrist operates is none of my business, but if he, as a doctor, can declare that a medical problem is not within his province to treat, then I, as a teacher, feel thoroughly justified in deciding that a case of bodily dysfunction — encopresis in this instance — is not an educational problem".

I was nettled, and in the manner of busybodies throughout the generations of Man who begin by declaring that the issue-at-hand is none of their business, I favoured the Social Worker with a lengthy résumé of medical and educational ethics, with my opinion of how they ought to inter-relate and where their boundaries lie, and was perorating very nicely thank you . . .

" . . . in this case the problem lies with the Psychiatrist, or, if he fails to do his duty, with the Health Authority which employs him. It is not **our** problem: **our** problem is The Child . . . "

. . . When a lady, holding a shopping-bag in front of her with both hands was followed by a radiantly-smiling Meg, carrying a dark-haired, bright-eyed little boy in the crook of her arm.

"This is Victor, Bryn, and this is Victor's mum". Victor looked at me unsmilingly, his thumb thrust firmly between his lips as if he knew what I had just been saying about him. His mother nodded and smiled nervously at the headmaster. Victor turned to bury his face in the soft hair of his new friend, who breezed on:

"We've had a really good talk in the classroom, Victor, his mum and I, and we've decided that he shall start school tomorrow morning. Even if we can't manage to arrange a taxi, Mrs. Wood is prepared to bring him herself".

"Ah! Just a moment, though. I was just explaining to Mrs. Jennings here that we . . . we haven't the facilities to . . . "

The Social Worker sprang to her feet. "I think I may be able to help there", and the three chattered away to each other in animated amity, while I stood there, another lonely Brand among the avalanche of his shattering principles, mouthing but not uttering.

Mrs. Jennings turned to me, her profession no doubt having accustomed her to the vagaries of the marital relationship. "Do you think I could use your telephone? I need to call the office to arrange a taxi".

In the car on our way home, I sought to reprove Meg.

"What about the **prin**ciple of this issue? Why should that psychiatrist be allowed to reject an obviously appropriate referral out of hand?"

"That's **his** problem, not ours. **Our** problem is the child; our problem is Victor. Isn't he a **lovely** little boy?"

Of course I didn't concede assent to my wife, but eventually even I had to agree with the Social Worker that Victor **was** a charming little lad, well-behaved, bright, alert and hard-working in the class-room. It was to transpire after not many weeks that he joined my map-reading excursions without risk, contributing to the discussion articulately in an unusually deep-toned voice for such a young child.

But for the moment Meg had opted into a grisly task.

Victor came to school equipped with a dozen pairs of underpants and three of short trousers, for he totally ignored immediate contact with the conventional discharge-points to the municipal sewage system, and his evacuation-frequency was more characteristic of the bladder than the rectum.

To be precise, it could not be said that Victor **suffered** from encopresis. His **mother** had suffered from it: **he** enjoyed it, positively revelling in the opportunities it gave him for faecal hand-printing and collage in the toilet and elsewhere in the house and garden.

Meg's early efforts sought to channel Victor's expressive energy towards more conventional art-forms, and here, as elsewhere, he proved an apt pupil in the course of time.

On his first morning in class he sat working hard at his desk without needing help. Then an odd sensation made its invisible presence felt. One after another of us uneasily lifted our heads, and our nostrils flared, like wild animals at an intruder's approach. The presence eddied and wafted from one part of the room to another. Victor's head remained down over his books.

Suddenly the full potency of the now all-pervading stench exploded, and, like deer affrighted in a forest glade, we arose, turned as one, and fled the room. Meg preserved the semblance of order by calling "Break-time", and herself removed the surprised Victor from the arena of the forore he had unwittingly caused.

Thenceforth Meg had Victor sitting next to her throughout class-times, and thus her nostrils were the early-warning system which divined Victor's colonic intimations, and she would spare the rest of us by whisking him away for her ministrations. She was learning to anticipate, but Victor had the advantage of her inexperience in this particular arena.

Notwithstanding, Meg's attitude towards Victor remained caring and loving, and only her husband noticed that, at times, her eyes were losing their focus, her smile becoming perceptibly crack-glazed. She showered daily immediately after school.

On one occasion, during Victor's second week, when they seemed to have been cloistered together an unusually long time, I knocked on the door.

"Can I help?"

"Just coming out", a faint voice responded.

The door opened, and the invisible fumes of fetor burst out and leapt at me like flames suddenly unconfined. I recoiled against the wall as Meg emerged, carrying Victor in a fireman's lift.

She bore him to the classroom, where she began carefully to seat him on one of the desks. She could not wholly disentangle from him because she found herself gently necklaced by Victor's arms, hand-clasped behind her. Surprised, she raised her face to his, and the 6-year-old boy made his first declaration of love, in his gruff Lancastrian brogue, as he looked deep into her eyes: "You're a grea-at girl".

De Profundis

For his fifteenth birthday, I had taken our John down that Sunday afternoon to Worcester, where the lustiness of Botham for his new County, and the flexuousness of Gower had pummelled, then massaged, then disengaged, the tension of my mind from its customary professional preoccupations.

We had motored on to the Malverns in the evening to pay our dues to the Beacons. Now I sat on the Worcestershire while John and our Welsh Springer vanished in an evening haze in a effort to reach the Herefordshire before nightfall.

On the way here the cab of the Unravelhome had resonated to Elgar's First Symphony, and now, sitting alone on the hard stone of the monument, there surged back into my mind — after the scarcely audible double-tremor of the drums, like the last echoes of a storm — the majestic opening. The haze lifted and the panorma was revealed below me. Surely it was **here** that he had composed It. As the full orchestra reached its climax, swirling in and about my head, I shared his Olympian overview of the Human Condition, and of my own human condition, with complete, but passionate disengagement. What Music! What a Composer! What a Man!

And yet . . . and yet . . . **what** a man? What sort of **man** was Elgar? That august melody which had filled my head was composed by a man who was a lifelong depressive, even at the height of his national eminence, a man who experienced profound uncertainties. A **life**long depressive, despite the boisterousness and the 'japes' of his young manhood. What had caused the existential fissure in this Great Man's assured and

130

successful demeanour? What storm had been echoing in **his** mind when he sat down to compose the first visionary notes of that Symphony.

Dusk closed in on me, and the townscape below was outlined by a reticulated sprinkling of tiny lights, as another melody by the same composer insinuated itself into my mind. The vibrant and sombrely elegaic voice of the cello recalled the one who bowed it, as if she had known of the imminent maiming of her faculties and of her early death. Cellist and composer, so harmoniously wedded in the performamce of 10 years before. Deepening dusk and a haze of non-meteorological origin obscured my vision, and I bethought myself of the composer as a man. Was he expressing an early sadness? What events in childhood had riven his soul to produce such a threnody?

Professional preoccupations returned. At about the time of the performance and recording which I had listened to so many times I was Care Taker in a day school for young children under stress.

I was having lunch at a table with three children, including 8-year-old Lisa, a sweet-natured, gentle-spoken child, whose major characteristic was the frequent, sudden exuding of perspiration, so that she always seemed to have just washed her hands without drying them.

There was an untypical, but a not uncompanionate, silence among our quartet, and we were just finishing our first course when I looked up to find Lisa sobbing almost noiselessly. I spoke, but she was helpless to reply. Her knife, dripping gravy, and fork still held in nerveless hands, slid to the edge of the table. I seized the cutlery and put them on the plate, and my voice joined the chorus of concerned enquiry. "What's up, Lisa?" "Are you alright?" "What's the matter?"

"George, did you . . . ?"

"No, Mister Purdy. I didn't do nuffin . . . this time".

Lisa's body was now racked by sobs as deep as a particularly virulent cough. It was crying of a kind which I had not witnessed in the five previous, and have not in fifteen subsequent, years. A concerned crowd had left their tables and were encircling ours. By now I was holding Lisa on to her chair, and she fell against my shoulder.

Feeling that action of some sort would help me, if it could do nothing for Lisa, I picked her up and carried her, one arm under her shoulders, the other under her knees, to the Staff Room. She lay in my lap, her head still limp on my shoulder and knuckles dug into her eyes. She was as profoundly unattainable to me as if she were undergoing a state of cataplexy, and I sat waiting for her to emerge from it.

As she came up from her depths, her sobs were exchanged for words, each one deeply emotionally-charged separately, but together having no meaning. I knew that they were clues to a deep disturbance, and awaited Lisa's return to consciousness when I might essay their piecing together into a coherent pattern.

It is a more 'normal' crying now. Lisa is surfacing again, looks round and is not surprised to find herself elsewhere, although she does not know how she arrived here. Snuffles. The accepting of paper tissues. A sitting-up. A tired smile. A shake of her hair to clear her eyes.

Unfamiliar situations precipitate new roles for me to play. Now I must be psychotherapist — for Lisa's sake, if not by qualification or experience.

"Can you remember what was upsetting you, Lisa?"

"Upsetting me?"

"Do you remember being upset?"

"You mean . . . crying like?" She is trying to help me, I know.

"Yes, crying. Do you remember crying?"

"Yeh, I were cryin' on your knee".

"Do you remember **why** you were crying?"

"No", helplessly shaking her head, and then brushing the hair out of her eyes again.

"Don't you remember saying . . . ?" and I spoke the several unconnected words she had uttered while she was in the depths of her despair.

"No. Did I say that?" A narrowing of her eyes in thought, and a puckering of her brows. "I 'member sittin' 'avin' me dinner when . . . when . . . I started cryin' . . ."

"Do you remember **why** you were crying? . . . What upset you?"

"No. I jus' remember startin' to cry at the dinner table . . ." And I could see that her mind was becoming engaged at another level of thought. "I'm 'ungry. Can we go for uz dinner?" She stood up, and extended her arm invitingly. I arose too, and clasped her hand ready to return to lunch.

"Let's go. Just a moment. Here's a couple of tissues for your hands".

"Oh, are they sweaty again?" A pretty placing of her other hand over her mouth in acknowledgement of the solecism, then she wiped both hands thoroughly and threw away the sodden tissues. "I'm sorry".

Her friend Mandy was anxiously waiting outside in the corridor, and arm-linked her warmly.

I relinquish Lisa to Mandy's total care, and follow the two little girls back to the dining-room, walking slowly and thoughtfully down the corridor . . .

. . . as I walk this evening, waving to my son in the near-darkness, as we two grope down a Malvern side to converge on the Unravelhome in the valley below, I speculating on the memories of this eight-year-old child, thoughts not too deep for tears, but too chasmed in her short past for recollection.

And, in a more general way, if this early childhood memory of Lisa's, precipitated not by petites madeleines but by meat and 2 veg., could have been so quickly forgotten — not so much an open wound to be examined as water closing over it — what chance for the rest of us? What chance have we to recall and understand childhood traumata which have caused our adult neuroses and unhappiness? What was it that Graham Greene had written in one of his essays? "Christ was betrayed in the childhood of Judas Iscariot".

Birth of a Book

Thanks for reading along with me so far. It *was* twins, by the way, but it's one of the advantages of book-bearing that you can stagger multiple births, that you can arrange the time of the accouchement with the printer to suit yourself — to be published in the Autumn ready for Christmas, for instance. And finding a printer was not as easy as you might think. The first one I approached had a conscientious objection to bad language. Wanted me to replace all the offending vowels with asterisks. But I discovered that I had a conscientious objection to disenvoweling books, so we had to call the deal off, amicably, as men of conscience should.

Oh yes, and the school did survive the financial threat of 1985. After entering that vertiginous hairpin bend, not knowing when — or whether — it might straighten out again, there was a holding of our overdraft during the following twelve months, and a gradual relaxing for the next two years, so that in 1988 the school has come starkly face-to-face with solvency.

There are so many other things I want to explain to you: the pronounciation of Caretaker, with the stress on the first syllable, as distinct from Care Taker, with its double stress and double meaning; the derivation and meaning of 'unravelhome'; and how a 'fictive documentary' is not a contradiction in terms (as a 'fictional documentary' would be). I had intended to tell you about Jane's canter in the Bull Ring of Birmingham (referred to in **A Policeman's Lot**), and about Befriending. I had intended to reveal to you the financial miracle which enabled a remaindered head teacher on the dole to purchase the premises which became the theatre of the dramas staged in the foregoing pages. I had inended to tell you how a dedicated co-educationalist like myself came to run a single-sex school; how such a one without apparent symptoms of masochism should choose to run a school for disturbed **girls**, and how the decision was randomly determined by a poem of Edward Thomas. But I shall have to desist till the next volume. What shall I call it? **Yobs and Grils**, perhaps, because I propose to include more anecdotes from my earlier professional life working with boys, to explain how I arrived at the egregious theories of childcare which have governed my maturity and precipitated my dotage. Or **Grils will be Girls**, perhaps, as I'd like to tell you how girls deemed to be 'maladjusted' in childhood develop into adulthood. Or, best of all, **What About us Grils?** memories of school-life told in the first person by the girls themselves.

Anyway, not another word. I must hie me to the printers. The manuscript, which has had a long and painful gestation as typescript, must become a book by Autumn, because my Meg wants to know how many copies will be left over to send out in December, in order to save on buying Christmas cards.